The Denver Catholic Biblical School Program

First Year
Old Testament Foundations: Genesis through Kings

STUDENT WORKBOOK

PAULIST PRESS

New York / Mahwah

Acknowledgements

The Publisher gratefully acknowledges use of the following materials: "Catholic Update" articles appearing in this workbook, originally published by St. Anthony Messenger Press, Cincinnati, Ohio; "The Desert: A 'Roundabout' Way," by Fr. Robert Wild, priest of Madonna House in Combermere, Ontario; "The Genesis of Liberation: Moses Bound and Unbound," by Lydia Champagne, C.S.J., reprinted from *The Bible Today* (January, 1981), by the Order of St. Benedict, Inc., published by The Liturgical Press, St. John's Abbey, Collegeville, Minnesota; "The Yahwist Passages from the Pentateuch," from *The Yahwist, The Bible's First Theologian*, by Peter F. Ellis, pp. 33–40, The Order of St. Benedict, Inc., published by The Liturgical Press, St. John's Abbey, Collegeville, Minnesota, reprinted with permission; "Father Abraham, My Friend and Mentor," originally published in *Liguorian*, reprinted with permission from *Liguorian*, One Liguori Drive, Liguori, MO, 63057; "On Burying Our Isaacs," by Mary Catherine Barron, from *Unveiled Faces: Men and Women of the Bible*, The Order of St. Benedict, Inc., published by The Liturgical Press, St. John's Abbey, Collegeville, Minnesota, reprinted with permission; "Yahweh: A Warrior God?" from *The Bible Today* (Peace Issue, May, 1983), published by The Liturgical Press, Collegeville, Minnesota 56321; "Elijah: Zealous for the Lord," by Marilyn Norquist, from *How To Read and Pray the Prophets,* copyright © 1980, by Liguori Publications. Used with permission. All rights reserved; "Commentary on the Isaac-Abraham Story," by Harvena Richter, Vol. XIV, number 4, October, 1984, p. 144, *Biblical Theology Bulletin, Inc.;* "And David Danced," by Mary E. Ingenthron, first published in *The Bible Today,* September, 1984, published by The Liturgical Press, Collegeville, Minnesota 56321.

"Special thanks are given to Mary Ingenthron for the biblical drawings that are included throughout this book."

Nihil Obstat:
   J. Anthony McDaid, J.C.D.

Imprimatur:
   ✠ J. Francis Stafford
   Archbishop of Denver
   Denver
   December 20, 1993

The Imprimatur is an official declaration that a book or pamphlet is free of doctrinal or moral error. No implication is contained therein that those who have granted the Imprimatur agree with the contents, opinions or statements expressed.

ISBN: 0-8091-9419-8

Published by Paulist Press
997 Macarthur Boulevard
Mahwah, NJ 07430

Printed and bound in the United States of America

CONTENTS

Foreword v

Student's Introduction...vii

Preparatory Lesson: Getting Ready to Read the Bible xiv

Unit One: The Exodus Experience...1

    I.1   The Call of Moses 2

    I.2   Plagues and Passover...4

    I.3   The Exodus 6

    I.4   The Desert 8

    I.5   Sinai 10

    I.6   The Ark of the Covenant..12

    I.7   The Golden Calf 14

    I.8   Torah: The Law...16

    I.9   Forty Years of Wandering..18

    I.10   Unit Review 20

Unit Two: Reflections on the Origins 21

    II.1   A New Focus on the Covenant...22

    II.2   Moses' Last Sermon and Death 24

    II.3   The Creation...26

    II.4   The Fall..28

    II.5   Noah, Babel 30

    II.6   Abraham, Covenant...32

    II.7   Abraham, Sodom, Isaac 34

    II.8   Isaac, Esau, Jacob...36

    II.9   Joseph 38

    II.10 Unit Review 40

Unit Three: Taking, Governing, Losing the Land..41

    III.1   The Conquest...42

    III.2   Charismatic Leaders: Gideon, Deborah, Samson................................44

    III.3   Kingship: Samuel and Saul...46

    III.4   Saul and David 48

    III.5   David and Nathan 50

    III.6   David and Absalom...52

    III.7   Solomon, The Divided Kingdom, Elijah 54

    III.8   Elisha and Athaliah 56

    III.9   The Fall of the Northern and Southern Kingdoms 58

    III.10 Final First Year Review...60

Supplementary Readings 61

1. More About Bible Translations 63

2. A Popular Guide to Reading the Bible 65

3. The Deliverance at the Sea 69

4. The Desert: A Roundabout Way 71

5. Why Is the Bible Like a Camel? 74

6. The Sources of the Pentateuch 79

7. Unit 1: Mid-Unit Self-Quiz 81

8. The Genesis of Liberation:
   Moses Bound and Unbound 83

9. Creation Myths from Other Cultures 87

10. The Yahwist Passages from the Pentateuch 89

11. Father Abraham, My Friend and Mentor 92

12. On Burying Our Isaacs 95

13. Biblical Heroes and Their Journeys of Faith 98

14. Yahweh: A Warrior God? 104

15. Heroic Women of the Bible 108

16. Self Quiz: The Deuteronomic History 113

17. Elijah: Zealous for the Lord 114

18. The Four-Year Study Plan of the Catholic Biblical School 117

Foreword

This book is the fruit of ten years of collaborative work in the Archdiocese of Denver. Archbishop James V. Casey of happy memory had a vision of a serious program of biblical study which would meet the needs and utilize the leadership potential of the many Catholics leaving the Catholic Church to attend fundamentalist Bible Colleges. He established the Catholic Biblical School in 1982. After his death it would expand greatly thanks to the support of Archbishop J. Francis Stafford.

Archbishop Casey entrusted the carrying out of his vision to me, and in time I was joined by teachers of outstanding competence and dedication: Steve Mueller, Ph.D., Angeline Hubert, Gene Giuliano, Dorothy Jonaitis, O.P., Kim Barta, and Kathy McGovern. Each contributed unique gifts to the development of the program.

We also received excellent organizational and clerical help from Tina Gargan, Audrey Jonas, Carol Perito, and Helen Williams. Without their support the cohesive program we have developed would have fallen apart at many places.

The most important collaborators of all have been our students—about 2,000 of them, each bringing a unique eagerness for the word of God and insight into it. Every detail of this program has been evaluated by them year after year and revised in the light of their experience.

Among the students who have been part of us from the very beginning, Mary Ingenthron has gifted us in a very special way with her creative talents. The illustrations in this book are among her many contributions.

We have also been blessed by the supervision of two Archdiocesan Directors of Catholic Education, Reverend Joseph M. O'Malley and Very Reverend J. Anthony McDaid, and the enthusiastic support of the priests and staff members of the archdiocese.

Through all of our shared work it has been evident that what has happened among us has been far beyond our combined ability; the Catholic Biblical School has been truly the work of the Spirit of God. It is our prayer that through this book this work of the Spirit may spread wherever people are hungry for God's word.

Macrina Scott, O.S.F.

Student's Introduction

Welcome to the journey of biblical study! We hope that your journey both will be pleasant and will also change your life. The journey of biblical study is not a geographical journey but a spiritual one. Reading the scriptures is a journey to the center of your faith. The goal of the journey is to learn about God and God's ways with us. Before our Christian faith was identified as Christian, it was simply called "the Way." Christianity is still "the way" to deepen our knowledge and experience of God at work in our world for our transformation. To follow the Christian way we must become familiar with God's ways as they are presented to us in the Bible.

The Bible is the church's book, or more realistically, the church's books. The Christian community existed before there were any Christian scriptures. The collection or canon of writings which make up the Bible are the ones that the church, through the guidance of the Holy Spirit, has recognized as special both in their production and in their importance for our lives. As Vatican Council II reminds us in its *Decree on Ecumenism*, "In the Church, according to Catholic belief, an authentic teaching office plays a special role in the explanation and the proclamation of the written word of God" (#21). For two thousand years the Bible has been normative and formative for our Christian life.

These books are normative for the church because they contain God's personal self-revelation to us in a unique way. "Those divinely revealed realities which are contained and presented in sacred scripture have been committed to writing under the inspiration of the Holy Spirit" and so "they have God as their author and have been handed on as such to the church herself. In composing the sacred books, God chose men and while employed by God they made use of their powers and abilities, so that with God acting in them and through them, they, as true authors, consigned to writing everything and only those things which God wanted" (Vatican II's *Dogmatic Constitution on Divine Revelation, Dei Verbum*, #11). Learning to read scripture means discovering God's message of salvation expressed by the many human voices struggling to proclaim the mystery of God.

These books are formative because reading them has shaped our Christian response to God's revelation. The biblical books have never been simply the object of scholarly study, but have always been used by the church for its theology, liturgy, prayer, spiritual direction, and moral guidance. By its reflection on scripture, the church has deepened its understanding of the mystery of God at work for salvation.

As the church has pondered the meaning of scripture throughout its lifetime, it has always been committed to understanding both the literal sense ("what meaning the sacred writers really intended") and the more than literal sense ("what God wanted to manifest by means of their words") (*Dei Verbum*, #12). Although the church has spoken very rarely on how to interpret individual verses of scripture, it has provided clear and helpful guidelines for how to interpret scripture so that we will not misread the meaning God intended to communicate through the words of the human author.

As members of the church, we must learn to read the Bible as the church intends us to. Our task is to understand the biblical message and apply it to our lives. Although we do not speak the same languages or share the same culture as the biblical authors, we have the same faith they did. We believe that God has been and is still active in our world for our salvation. By using the biblical accounts of how God has guided our world toward salvation, we can discover God now at work for salvation in our world.

Preparing for the Journey

Before you embark on your journey you need to make some preparations. What will you take along to help the trip go more smoothly? The first requirement for any trip into unfamiliar territory would be a good map. Your map for journeying through the many different books of the Bible is the program developed by the Catholic Biblical School of the Archdiocese of Denver. Since 1982, the Denver Catholic Biblical School has been directing adults who desire a deeper knowledge of scripture through the process of reading and interpreting the Bible. In its first ten years more than two thousand adults have been enrolled in this program. Almost five hundred students completed the entire four-year course. Their enthusiasm and their accomplishment indicate that this program works.

We encourage the approach to Bible interpretation recommended by Vatican Council II in its *Dogmatic Constitution on Divine Revelation, Dei Verbum*. Since the Bible is first of all the church's book, you must learn to read it and interpret it according to the directives provided by the church. This Council document summarizes almost two thousand years of the church's wisdom and experience in appropriating God's message expressed in the human words of the Bible. Unless you read and understand this document, you will not be in step with the way that the church teaches us to approach reading and understanding the Bible.

Even if you are not a Catholic, this contextual approach is still the most suitable one for determining the meaning intended by the biblical author.

Dei Verbum section #12 outlines the basic steps necessary for a correct understanding of scripture. The document wisely reminds us that the goal of scripture study is the understanding of *MEANING*, which demands locating a text within its contexts. This contextual approach to meanings demands two adjustments often neglected in scripture study. First, it means moving beyond simple catchwords as a clue to the meaning of scripture. We cannot assume that every use of a word, which can be gleaned from a concordance of words in scripture, is the same. The meaning depends on the context. Words become meaningful only in the larger contexts of sentences, paragraphs, chapters, books and finally the whole of the Bible. Second, it also means recognizing that facts and meaning are not simply identical. Facts are not meaningful in themselves but only when their significance is noted by placing them in a context. To say that Jesus died on the cross is a fact, but Romans, Jews, and Christians interpreted the meaning of this fact very differently because of their different contexts or perspectives.

The document then identifies three specific contexts which must be looked at in order to come to an understanding of the author's intended meaning. The first step recognizes the *LITERARY CONTEXT*. We must learn to read the texts according to the best methods of interpretation of literature, and in particular we must not confuse types of literature. God was not limited to inspiring only one type of writing. The Bible contains various types of literature—poetry, prophecy, different kinds of history, letters, parables, stories, and other types of writing. To know how to read a text without confusion, we must determine what kind of writing it is and read it according to the rules appropriate for the style in which it was written.

The second step investigates the *HISTORICAL CONTEXT*. Since we must learn to interpret texts in their own historical time and in the specific situations in which they were composed, the more we can learn about the historical events which form the background for the biblical writings, the better we can discover what the author was trying to communicate. This also helps us to recognize when we are imposing our own ideas on the text. In their own times, for example, the Jewish prophets were directing their words to their contemporaries in order to solve their problems. They were not looking hundreds of years or centuries into the future to speak concretely about Jesus or to solve our problems today. Although we can use the texts for these purposes, we must recognize that this was not the intention in the mind of the original author when the texts were composed.

The third step examines the *SOCIAL (CULTURAL) AND RHETORICAL CONTEXT*. Reading the Bible is like a trip to a foreign country. Not only do we have to translate the words of the Bible into our language, but we need to be aware of the cultural context in which these words made sense. The way the ancient authors and their audiences thought and spoke and organized their everyday world was very different from ours. We must study the cultural situation out of which the texts came in order to understand the message the author was trying to convey to the original audience. Paul, for example, wrote his letters in a way that his community would understand but which we might find hard to grasp because of our different ways of communicating.

Attending to these three contexts will provide us with an understanding of the literal sense of scripture which the sacred writers intended. But the church has always realized that what the author intended never exhausts

the meaning of the text. Other meanings arise because the scriptures are always interpreted in new contexts which the authors never foresaw. Through the help of the Holy Spirit, the church directs us to search for the further meanings "which God wanted manifest by their words." These meanings come to light as the faithful reflect upon the meaning of scripture and as the teaching office of the church serves the word by "teaching only what has been handed on, listening to it devoutly, guarding it scrupulously, and explaining it faithfully by divine commission and with the help of the Holy Spirit" (*Dei Verbum*, #10).

The document suggests two particular ways of discovering these other meanings. First of all, we must attend to the "content and unity of the whole of Scripture." How easily we forget that the authors of scripture did not set out to write a new book of scripture or that when the New Testament authors wrote there was no "New Testament" to which they could compare their work. Because we have the whole Bible, we can recognize the interconnectedness of themes, the growth and development of understanding which occurs even within the Bible between earlier books and later ones, and the way later authors depend upon earlier ones. This is one reason that our program studies all the books of the Bible and not just a selected few.

Second, we are directed to take into consideration the "living tradition of the whole Church along with the harmony which exists between elements of faith." There is a long tradition of how the church has understood and used the scriptures for theology, spiritual and moral guidance, prayer and liturgy. Sections #7–9 of *Dei Verbum* summarize the ways that this living tradition develops in the church to bring out the further meanings and preserve the full integrity of God's communication to us. As we study the scriptures, we become more sensitive to the ways that the message of scripture is communicated to us through the church's teaching, through the teaching of bishops, through homilies every Sunday and through our sharing with others each week the fruits of our prayerful reflection and study.

But after our search for the meaning of the text, we must finally make the *APPLICATION* of this meaning to our situation today. This application is essential, and can be done well only if we have considered as thoroughly as possible what the text meant in its original situation and in the living tradition of the church community. We must also carefully examine our own presuppositions for applying the text. Some people read the Bible simply for "proof-texts" to support their own positions. Others reduce God's message to abstract theological or moral ideas. We must recognize that these approaches can greatly limit a fuller grasp of the meaning of God's message for us.

Books for Your Journey

Unlike many other adult study programs, this program covers the whole of the Bible during the course of four years. The main focus of study is the Bible text itself rather than any books about the Bible. Nothing can replace your own familiarity with the biblical text as the core of your study. The lessons have been arranged to take you through a comprehensive reading of the biblical text in a way that helps you to understand its arrangement, its composition, and its relationship with other biblical texts.

So, for your journey, you must have a good Bible. A good study Bible ought to have both the best translation possible and scholarly notes which provide help as you read. We recommend the *New American Bible*, with the newly revised translation of the New Testament (1986) and the Psalms (1992). The best

edition of this translation comes in the Oxford *Catholic Study Bible*, which also contains articles and study guides for the student. Some might prefer the *New Jerusalem Bible*. Although its translation is often more British rather than American English, its notes are excellent. You might also like to use the *Revised Standard Version* or the recently updated *New Revised Standard Version*, but make sure that you purchase the annotated version with the Apocryphal books. We recommend the *Oxford Annotated Bible with the Apocrypha*. (Most of these "apocryphal" books are called deuterocanonical books by Catholics and accepted as part of the Bible.) The notes in this version are adequate but not quite as extensive as the *New American*. For more on choosing a Bible see #1, "More About Bible Translations" in the SUPPLEMENTARY READINGS at the end of this book.

To prepare yourself for your journey, you might wish to read a book which helps orient you to Bible study — for example, Fr. Daniel A. Murray's *The Living Word in the Living Church: A Guide to What Every Catholic Should Know about Scripture, Tradition, and The Teaching Office* [Thomas Nelson,1986], or George Martin's *Reading Scripture as the Word of God: Practical Approaches and Attitudes* (2nd ed.) [Servant Books, 1982] and "A Popular Guide to Reading the Bible," by Sr. Macrina Scott, O.S.F., the founder and Director of the Catholic Biblical School, #2 in your SUPPLEMENTARY READINGS. The Oxford *Catholic Study Bible* also contains some excellent introductory articles for you to study.

Just as you might like a tour guide to give you background and history about the places you are seeing or visiting, so we recommend John L. McKenzie's *Dictionary of the Bible* [Macmillan, 1967]. Not only does this book provide excellent material about the people, places, things and themes of the Bible, but it also provides superb theological information which goes far beyond most dictionaries of the Bible.

It is also very helpful to have an atlas of biblical lands for the many maps you will need to consult to find the historical and geographical places mentioned in the Bible. We recommend the inexpensive *Hammond Atlas of the Bible Lands*. However there are many other fine atlases available.

For each unit of study, we will also recommend textbooks that we have found helpful for our own students. Many of these are general books, such as Lawrence Boadt's *Reading the Old Testament* [Paulist, 1984], which can be used during several different units. These books will form the backbone of your own personal scripture reference library.

Making the Journey

For your adventure of biblical study, our weekly materials will be your most detailed map. These assignments will give you guidance for reading and reflecting on the specific message of each book. Although you might be tempted to make the journey as fast as you can, there are no short cuts. The Bible is a library of books, and it takes a long time to work through it. The weekly readings divide the material into manageable chunks for you to work on. Remember, reading the biblical passages is always the most important thing to do. No amount of reading about the Bible can substitute for reading the Bible itself.

The weekly assignment questions are like trail markers on your "pathways through scripture." By following them, you will be led into the text of the Bible to discover the treasures that are hidden there. Don't look for the answers in scholarly commentaries and textbooks. Answer the assignment questions from your own reading of the text and from your own reflection and thought.

As you follow the trail markers, though, do not be afraid to venture off to investigate other things which spark your interest. We provide "optional challenges" each week which suggest some possible things you can investigate or do to deepen your experience of the lesson for the week.

Do not be limited by our suggestions. Whatever fascinates you, excites your wonder, or provokes a question for you is a good place to branch off from the main path to do your own private exploration. What you explore through these optional challenges is something to share with the others on your journey who have not had the time or perhaps the interest to follow up as you have. You give them a great gift when you share your optional challenges.

Although the optional challenges explicitly suggest that you transfer what you have learned into another form, e.g., a song, poem, skit, cartoon, etc., we encourage you to do this on your own as often as possible. We have had students who took the initiative to do such projects as weavings representing each of the books studied, timelines, maps, family trees to keep the characters straight, modern day parables, myths, dramatic skits, mimes of the passion, etc. By presenting the material in another form, you deepen your knowledge of the biblical message and learn new ways to proclaim it.

We also suggest a memory verse for your use each week. These memory verses that we have put in our own translation serve a dual purpose. First of all, they help you to make passages from scripture your own. The thoughts and words from the Bible become your own as you repeat them. It is always helpful to compare different translations in order to notice how the translators have tried to convey the meaning of the original language.

Second, the memory verses help you to pray the scriptures. Sometimes the study of the biblical text each week can turn into just another intellectual exercise. But by praying over the memory verse, you touch the deeper dimension of the scripture as God's word for you. The memory verse can be recited at different times of the day. Thus it is a reminder of your lesson and the ways that the lesson can be made part of your life.

Companions for Your Journey

Although you could use this program to make the journey through the Bible alone, you will be using these materials for group study. Much of the fun of a journey, a pilgrimage or a vacation comes by sharing it with others. Sightseeing or discovering new places takes on a new dimension when we share it with others.

So likewise, sharing what we have discovered each week is more beneficial if we do it with a group of like-minded scripture pilgrims. Besides, we can learn much from the ideas and insights of others who often perceive the meaning of a passage more deeply because of their own life experience. For example, we have had blind and handicapped students who have shared what it is like to feel the healing power of Jesus breaking into their lives. Their unique perspective supplements ours and enriches our appreciation of the many dimensions of scripture.

For our Catholic Biblical School program, we have devised some helps for making the group process run more smoothly. Since these guidelines provide you with directives for your weekly small group discussions, we call them:

The Ten Commandments of Group Process

1. Work to build trust and intimacy within your group.

2. Get to the heart of the passage.
    Don't just skim the surface.

3. Give everyone in your group a chance to talk.
    No speeches!

4. Speak connectedly with previous speakers.
    Consciously work at building bridges with what has already been said.

5. While one person speaks, everyone else listens.

6. Never ridicule or cut down another's answers.

7. When you disagree, do so with respect.

8. Do not fear silence.

9. If you have not done your homework, answer only the questions which your instructor designates.

10. Enjoy yourself!

Advice from the Experts

When venturing out on a journey, it is often helpful to ask people who have already made the trip for advice. We have received input from many of our graduates who have finished the entire four-year course. Their reflections might prove useful as you begin your journey.

Perhaps the most important advice is their simple and oft repeated encouragement: "Don't be afraid." Fear cripples your learning. Your learning is beginning, so don't think that you have to know it all already! If you don't have any questions, then you probably won't be learning much either.

Doing your reading, reflecting, and writing each week demands a serious commitment of both time and energy. Try, if at all possible, not to fall behind. The tendency once you fall behind is to short-change the work just to get it done. The old saying that you get out of it what you put into it is also true for your studies. Skimpy work yields skimpy results.

Be open to the unexpected challenges which will arise as you read and study each week. As Vatican II reminds us, the scriptures are different from other things we read because they contain God's self-revelation in an inspired and inerrant way. As we work on God's word, God's word also works on us. Our cherished assumptions, our values, our attitudes and our actions might all be challenged as we discover God's ways in our world.

Concerning your group discussion time, recognize that each person in the group is your teacher in some way or other. We learn from each other if we pay close attention. It is amazing how we read the same words but interpret and respond to them so differently. This is the richness of our shared group experience.

Don't be afraid to share what you are learning with your family and friends. They sacrifice much so that you can find the time to study and attend class each week. Your sharing with them is not only your first step as a minister of God's word, but through your sharing our biblical heritage can once again become the foundation of the religious life of the family.

So, as your journey begins, be open to where the Lord wishes to lead you. The word of God is a treasure which we will never exhaust. It is also a challenge which causes us to change our lives. God's word has been given for us to know it, to love it, and finally to live it. Welcome to the most fascinating, the most rewarding, and sometimes the most frustrating journey of your life. Enjoy it!

GETTING READY TO READ THE BIBLE

Goal: To become familiar with the Catholic church's contextual approach to understanding the meaning of scripture and with terms commonly used regarding scripture interpretation.

Reading Boadt, *Reading the Old Testament*, pp. 11-26; Vatican II's *Dogmatic Constitution on Divine Revelation* [*Dei Verbum*] (read the entire document and note in particular the excerpts on the following page); entries in McKenzie's *Dictionary of the Bible* on Revelation, Inspiration, Interpretation, Bible, Text, Septuagint, Vulgate, English Versions, Literary Forms.

Assignment Questions

1. Using the selections from Vatican II's *Dei Verbum*, describe the following:

   Revelation   Inerrancy
   Inspiration   Canon

2. How are the books of the Bible arranged in Jewish Bibles? in Catholic Bibles? in Protestant Bibles? How might these different arrangements make each group think differently about the meaning of God's activity in our world for salvation?

3. How do you understand the meaning of McKenzie's statement that:

   "what God means in the Bible can be investigated only by discovering what the human author means, since God does not make His meanings known except through the human writer" (*Dictionary of the Bible*, p. 393).

4. *Dei Verbum* #12 states that "truth is proposed and expressed in a variety of ways." What examples from your own life can you think of to illustrate this?

5. In what way has reading these materials clarified or changed your thinking about revelation, inspiration, or biblical interpretation?

6. As we begin any project, it helps to reflect upon our own motives and goals. Write a statement of your goals, using the following questions to help you.

   What you want from Bible study?
   Why is it important for you to do it?
   What do you expect to find when you read the Bible?
   How has the Bible provided you with clues about God's saving work in your life?

Optional Challenge Give a brief definition for each of the following terms:

   Septuagint   Pseudepigrapha
   Masoretic Text   Testament
   Deuterocanonical   Literary Genre
   Apocrypha   Pentateuch

Important Excerpts from Vatican II's
Dogmatic Constitution on Divine Revelation [Dei Verbum]

#2.   In His goodness and wisdom, God chose to reveal Himself and to make known to us the hidden purpose of His will by which through Christ, the Word made flesh, man has access to the Father in the Holy Spirit and comes to share in the divine nature. Through this revelation, therefore, the invisible God out of the abundance of His love speaks to men as friends and lives among them so that He might invite and take them into fellowship with Himself. This plan of revelation is realized by deeds and words having an inner unity: the deeds wrought by God in the history of salvation manifest and confirm the teachings and realities signified by the words, while the words proclaim the deeds and clarify the mystery contained in them. By this revelation, then, the deepest truth about God and the salvation of humanity is made clear to us in Christ, who is the Mediator and at the same time the fullness of all revelation.

#10.   Sacred tradition and sacred Scripture form one sacred deposit of the word of God, which is committed to the Church. Holding fast to this deposit, the entire holy people united with their shepherds remain always steadfast in the teaching of the apostles, in the common life, in the breaking of the bread, and in prayers, so that in holding to, practicing, and professing the heritage of the faith, there results on the part of the bishops and faithful a remarkable common effort.

The task of authentically interpreting the word of God, whether written or handed on, has been entrusted exclusively to the living teaching office of the Church, whose authority is exercised in the name of Jesus Christ. This teaching office is not above the word of God, but serves it, teaching only what has been handed on, listening to it devoutly, guarding it scrupulously, and explaining it faithfully by divine commission and with the help of the Holy Spirit; it draws from this one deposit of faith everything which it presents for belief as divinely revealed.

It is clear, therefore, that sacred tradition, sacred Scripture, and the teaching authority of the Church, in accord with God's most wise design, are so linked and joined together that one cannot stand without the others, and that all together and each in its own way under the action of the one Holy Spirit contribute effectively to the salvation of souls.

#11.   Those divinely revealed realities which are contained and presented in sacred Scripture have been committed to writing under the inspiration of the Holy Spirit. Holy Mother Church, relying on the belief of the apostles, holds that the books of both the Old and New Testament in their entirety, with all their parts, are sacred and canonical because, having been written under the inspiration of the Holy Spirit, they have God as their author and have been handed on as such to the Church herself. In composing the sacred books, God chose men and while employed by God they made use of their powers and abilities, so that with God acting in them and through them, they, as true authors, consigned to writing everything and only those things which God wanted.

Therefore, since everything asserted by the inspired authors or sacred writers must be held to be asserted by the Holy Spirit, it follows that the books of Scripture must be acknowledged as teaching firmly, faithfully, and without error that truth which God wanted put into the sacred writings for the sake of our salvation. Therefore, "all Scripture is inspired by God and useful for teaching, for reproving, for correcting, for instruction in justice; that the man of God may be perfect, equipped for every good work" (2 Tim. 3:16-17).

#12.   However, since God speaks in sacred Scripture through men in human fashion, the interpreter of sacred Scripture, in order to see clearly what God wanted to communicate to us, should carefully investigate what meaning the sacred writers really intended, and what God wanted to manifest by means of their words.

Those who search out the intention of the sacred writers must, among other things, have regard for the "literary forms." For truth is proposed and expressed in a variety of ways, depending on whether a text is history of one kind or another, or whether its form is that of prophecy, poetry, or some other type of speech. The interpreter must investigate what meaning the sacred writer intended to express and actually expressed in particular circumstances as he used contemporary literary forms in accordance with the situation of his own time and culture. For the correct understanding of what the sacred author wanted to assert, due attention must be paid to the customary and characteristic styles of perceiving, speaking, and narrating which prevailed at the time of the sacred writer, and to the customs people normally followed at that period in their everyday dealings with one another.

But, since holy Scripture must be read and interpreted according to the same Spirit by whom it was written, no less serious attention must be given to the content and unity of the whole of Scripture, if the meaning of the sacred texts is to be correctly brought to light. The living tradition of the whole Church must be taken into account along with the harmony which exists between elements of the faith. It is the task of exegetes to work according to these rules toward a better understanding and explanation of the meaning of sacred Scripture, so that through preparatory study the judgment of the Church may mature. For all of what has been said about the way of interpreting Scripture is subject finally to the judgment of the Church, which carries out the divine commission and ministry of guarding and interpreting the word of God.

AN OVERVIEW OF YEAR ONE — UNIT ONE
The Exodus Experience

Objectives   1. To learn to work with the biblical text, alone and in a group, using the footnotes and various translations.

2. To understand the biblical concepts of liberation, covenant, the people of God and the law.

3. To come to know Moses and Miriam as part of your own faith community, with something to say to you.

4. To learn the process by which the Book of Exodus (and other biblical books) took shape, and to begin to distinguish the principal sources.

Textbooks   Primary text: The Bible. Use a good translation with scholarly notes. For more information on choosing a Bible see #1, "More About Bible Translations," in the SUPPLEMENTARY READINGS at the end of this book.

Other texts: For helpful background and handy reference we recommend:
John L. McKenzie   *Dictionary of the Bible* (cited as MDB)
Lawrence Boadt   *Reading the Old Testament*
Hammond's   *Atlas of Bible Lands*

Assignments   Each lesson is to be studied in preparation for your group discussion. For each biblical passage, you should do the assigned readings and answer in writing the questions given.

I.1   THE CALL OF MOSES ....Exodus 1–6

I.2   PLAGUES AND PASSOVER..Exodus 7–13

I.3   THE EXODUS..Exodus 14–15

I.4   THE DESERT ....Exodus 16–18

I.5   SINAI..Exodus 19–24

I.6   THE ARK OF THE COVENANT..Exodus 25–31, 40

I.7   THE GOLDEN CALF...Exodus 24:12–18, 32–34

I.8   TORAH: THE LAW...Leviticus 12–14, 16, 19, 23, 26

I.9   FORTY YEARS WANDERING.....................................Numbers 6, 9–14, 16, 17, 20–24

I.10 UNIT REVIEW

I.1: The Call of Moses

Read: Exodus 1–6

1. A. Why did Pharaoh persecute the Hebrews?
    B. Why do you think that he allowed the girls to live when he killed the boys?
    C. Why do you think other persecutions of minorities have taken place throughout history?

2. According to Genesis 25:1–2, from whom were the Midianites descended?

3. Draw a family tree or chart showing Moses' parents, brother, sister, wife, father-in-law, and sons (his second son is mentioned in Ex 18:4). To what tribe did they belong?

4. How did Moses respond to Yahweh's call? Have you ever experienced a "call" in your life? Describe the experience.

5. A. List the problems Moses faced in freeing the Israelites. Give the chapter and verse when describing each problem.
    B. How are they similar to the problems faced by those struggling for freedom and justice today?

6. A. What character traits of Moses do you see in these chapters? Give references with chapter and verse.
    B. Why do you think that God chose a person of this type to lead Israel out of Egypt?

> *Earth's crammed with*
> *heaven, and every common*
> *bush afire with God;*
> *but only he who sees*
> *takes off his shoes —*
> *the rest sit down and*
> *pluck blackberries.*
>
> *— Elizabeth Barrett Browning*

> *God has made a people for Himself and to show the intimacy of the alliance He reveals to this people His name, that is to say, His personal being. God reveals Himself as a Person whom one can invoke and who responds to the call of people; the Covenant inaugurates interpersonal relations between God and His people.*
>
> *— Rene Latourelle*, Revelation, History and Incarnation

SUGGESTIONS FOR THE STUDENT

After studying this lesson, you should:

1. Be able to identify the following people: Moses, Miriam, Aaron, Pharaoh, Pharaoh's daughter, Jochebed, Amram, Zipporah, and Jethro.

2. Know the basic outline of the story of Israel's oppression and Moses' call.

3. Be able to identify the five books of the Pentateuch.

4. Be able to locate Egypt on a map.

Memory Verse Suggestion:

Exodus 6:5 — "I have heard the groaning of the people of Israel whom the Egyptians hold in bondage and I have remembered my covenant."

Exodus 2:3–4 Miriam watches over Moses

I.2: Plagues and Passover

Read: Exodus 7–13; MDB articles: "Plagues of Egypt" and "Passover"; Boadt, Chapter 1, pp. 11–26.

1. The Bible describes the plagues as a "sign," i.e., events that carried a message from God. Can you think of any event in your life which was such a "sign" for you?

2. List some similarities between the plagues in Revelation 16 and those in Exodus. Give chapter and verse numbers in your comparison.

3. What religious ritual must a man have undergone before he could participate in the Passover? Cite the chapter and verse where the answer is found.

4. Scholars say that John 19:31–36 shows that John, the gospel writer, considered Jesus to be like the lamb eaten at Passover. What passage in Exodus leads them to that conclusion?

5. Read Psalm 105:1–7, 23–38. Compare the description of the events with that given in the Book of Exodus. Does the psalm give you any new insights or feeling for the experience?

Exercises   The exercises are part of the required study but do not need to be written.

A. Notice how frequently the idea of worship is mentioned in these chapters.
B. Notice how Moses becomes more outspoken and Pharaoh more willing to negotiate as the plagues progress.

Optional Challenge

1. What resemblances do you see between the Passover Haggadah and our Christian Eucharistic liturgy?

2. Assume that you are Pharaoh. Write a diary of your experiences with Moses and the Israelites.

> It is irrelevant whether "much" or "little," unusual things or usual, tremendous or trifling events happened; what is vital is only that what happened was experienced, while it was happening, as the act of God. The people saw in whatever it was they saw "the great hand," and they "believed in YHVH," or, more correctly translated, they gave their trust to YHVH. We have found that the permissible concept of miracle from the historical approach means, to begin with, nothing but an abiding astonishment.
>
> — Martin Buber, Moses

SUGGESTIONS FOR THE STUDENT

After studying this lesson, you should:

1. Be able to explain the basic elements of the Passover liturgy and to know their relationship to the Exodus experience.

2. Recognize the connection between the Passover and the paschal mystery of Jesus.

Memory Verse Suggestion:

Exodus 7:5 —   "And the Egyptians shall know that I am the Lord, when I stretch forth my hand upon Egypt and bring out the people of Israel from among them."

Other Exercises:

If you want to do more reading on the comparison of the Passover Haggadah and our Christian Eucharist, some useful books are:

The Passover Haggadah edited by Nahum Glazer (Schocken Books)
Guide to Jewish Holy Days: History & Observance by Hayyim Schauss (Schocken Books)

For the Christian perspective, see:

Jesus and Passover by Anthony J. Salardini (Paulist)
The Eucharistic Words of Jesus by Joachim Jeremias

Exodus 12:30   Pharaoh mourns child

I.3: The Exodus

Read: Exodus 14–15; MDB: "Exodus" (before the article on "Exodus, Book of");
Boadt, Chapter 8, pp. 155–172.

1. A. What time of day does the passage through the Sea of Reeds take place?
    B. What time do you think that the Resurrection of Jesus took place?
    C. What annual Catholic liturgical celebration takes place at the same time as
        the passage through the Sea of Reeds and has a similar theme?

2. List several facts that could be learned about Miriam from this passage.
    Give chapter and verse where each fact is found.

3. A. How do the Israelites feel about being liberated from their Egyptian slavery?
    B. Are we Christians today ever like them? Give examples.

4. Scholars believe that two main traditions [JE and P] about the passage through
    the sea have been combined to make up Chapters 13–14 of Exodus. You will
    find a reconstruction by modern scholars of these two traditions in "Deliverance
    at the Sea," #3 in your SUPPLEMENTARY READINGS. Use this reading rather than
    your Bible to answer these questions.

    A. Describe briefly and concretely what happened according to JE and then
        according to P. Do NOT quote the Bible, but summarize so as to present
        the bare facts. Be sure to read each account separately as it appears in your
        SUPPLEMENTARY READINGS #3.

    B. What major differences do you see between the two accounts?

Optional   1. Research and report on theories of scholars regarding the location of the
Challenge   Sea of Reeds.

2. If you had been a reporter for an Egyptian newspaper, how might you have
    reported the incident at the sea?

3. If you had written editorials for an Egyptian newspaper, how might you have com-
    mented on the incident?

SUGGESTIONS FOR THE STUDENT

After studying this lesson, you should:

1. Be able to name the three sources found in Exodus:
   Yahwist (J), Elohist (E), and Priestly (P).

2. Note that the sea involved is the Sea of Reeds, not the Red Sea.

3. Recognize the distinction between the prose and poetic versions of the story.

4. See the significance of trust in God in the events at the sea.

Memory Verse Suggestion:

Exodus 15:2 —   "The Lord is my strength and my song,
                        and he has become my salvation;
                        this is my God, and I will praise him,
                        my father's God, and I will exalt him."

Exodus 14:13, 14 —   "Fear not, stand firm, and see the salvation of the Lord
                        which God will do for you today . . .
                        The Lord will fight for you,
                        you have only to stand still.

Exodus 15:20   Miriam's song

I.4: The Desert

Read: Exodus 16–18; MDB: "Desert" and "Manna."
                 "The Desert: A Roundabout Way," #4 in your SUPPLEMENTARY READINGS.

1. The theme of grumbling dominates Chapter 16.
   A. List the verses in Chapter 16 which mention the idea of grumbling or complaining.
   B. Can you think of situations today where grumbling is a problem?

2. Read Chapter 6 of John's gospel. What indications do you find there that the gospel writer had these chapters of Exodus in mind? Give at least three scripture references.

3. A. To what text in this week's reading does Paul refer in 1 Corinthians 10:1–5?
   B. Why do you think St. Paul sees the rock as an image of Jesus?

4. A. What part did Moses play in the war with Amalek?
   B. Do you see any significance for your life in the account of the war with Amalek? If so, what?

5. Jethro is not a member of the chosen people. What words and actions of his seem surprising for one who is not an Israelite?

Exercise   Read through the list of abbreviations on page ix of the *Dictionary of the Bible*.

Optional   1. Write a prayer or song or poem or do some art work that expresses something
Challenge   of the meaning of Exodus, chapters one through eighteen.

Great issues affecting humankind always have to be decided in the wilderness, in uninterrupted isolation and unbroken silence. They hold a meaning and a blessing, these great, silent empty spaces, that bring us face to face with reality. . . . The wilderness has a necessary function in life. "Abandonment" one of my friends called it, and the word is very apt. Abandonment to wind and weather and day and night and all the intervening hours. And abandonment to the silence of God, the greatest abandonment of all. The virtue that thrives most on it — patience — is the most necessary of all virtues that spring from the heart — and the Spirit.

                                                                    — *Fr. Alfred Delp*
                                                                    Written while in a Nazi prison

SUGGESTIONS FOR THE STUDENT

After studying this lesson, you should:

1. See Israel's experience in the desert as a time of growth and trust as well as a time of grumbling and complaint.

2. Recognize the desert experience as part of our spirituality.

3. Be able to identify the following: manna, Massah and Meribah, Amalek, Jethro, Joshua, and Hur.

Memory Verse Suggestion:

Exodus 16:11–12 — And the Lord said to Moses,
"I have heard the murmurings of the people of Israel;
say to them, 'At twilight you shall eat flesh,
and in the morning you shall be filled with bread;
then you shall know that I am the Lord your God.'"

Other Exercises:

Think of an experience in your life which was like the desert for the Israelites.
Share this with the members of your discussion group.

Exodus 17:12–13 Aaron and Hur support Moses

I.5: Sinai

Read: Exodus 19–24; MDB: "Sinai."

1. A. Between what two parties is the covenant made?
    B. What is the role of Moses?

2. What similarities do you see between:
    A. Moses' experience of God in Exodus 3 and the experience of the people in Exodus 19 and Exodus 20?
    B. Between either of these and Matthew 17:1–8?

3. What meaning do you think the first commandment (Ex 20:2–6) has for us today?

4. A. What reason is given for the Sabbath observance in
        1) Exodus 20:8–11
        2) Exodus 23:12
        3) Deuteronomy 5:14–15
        (Clue: each gives a different motive or reason for the observance.)
    B. Why and how should we observe the Lord's Day?

5. Give examples of laws in Chapters 21–23 which express special concern for the poor and those unable to protect themselves. Cite chapter and verse number.

6. A. Do you notice any law in Chapters 21–23 which would not apply to the Israelites during their forty years of nomadic life in the desert? Cite chapter and verse.
    B. How would you account for the presence of these laws in the text?

Exercise   Notice how these chapters are used in Hebrews 12:18–29.

Optional Challenge

1. List the references to fire and cloud in Exodus so far.

2. Why do you think these are chosen as symbols of God's presence?

3. Read Matthew 5–7.
    A. What similarities do you see between Jesus' instructions and the law as it is given in Exodus?
    B. What differences? Be specific.

SUGGESTIONS FOR THE STUDENT

After studying this lesson, you should:

1. Know the meaning of the term "covenant."

2. Be able to locate Sinai (the traditional site) on a map.

3. Be able to identify the terms: Decalogue, Covenant Code, and Torah.

4. Understand the pre-eminent role of the Sinai experience in the history of Israel and her sense of being a people of God.

Memory Verse Suggestion:

Exodus 19:4 —   "I bore you on eagles' wings,
                  and brought you here to Myself."

Israel never thought of the Decalogue as a set of ten "commandments," that is, as anonymous collections of prohibitions and taboos, but rather as "words of God.". . . It is part of the covenant dialogue which God enters into with his people. It is as if God were saying to his people: "If you want to enter upon the covenant, here are the words for your dialogue with me. By keeping them you will become my people and I shall remain your God.". . . When Israel thinks of the ten words of the covenant, it does not start sighing as though it were contemplating a burden, or groaning as though it were weighed down by them; its attitude is one of gratitude and praise. God's word is refreshment for the soul, joy for the heart, light for the eyes; it is more desirable than purest gold, sweeter than syrup or honey from the comb (Ps 19:8–15). In receiving it, Israel did not receive a set of police regulations, but its own freedom, not chains, but the bonds that tenderness creates.

— *Lucien Deiss,* God's Word and God's People

Exodus 18:19ff Jethro's advice to Moses

I.6: The Ark of the Covenant

Read: Exodus 25–31 and 40; MDB: "Ark of the Covenant"; Sr. Macrina Scott, "Why is the Bible like a Camel?" #5 in your SUPPLEMENTARY READINGS.

1. List some materials and colors mentioned in connection with the tabernacle and Ark. Put a check mark beside those which are in liturgical use today.

2. List the kinds of craftspersons who would be necessary to build the Ark and tabernacle as described in these chapters.

3. Read Exodus 31:1–6.
    A. What specific skills are needed in a modern parish to enrich the liturgy?
    B. How do you think the skills of parishioners could be more effectively used in your parish liturgy?
    C. What can you do to see that these skills are utilized?

4. A. What symbols or symbolic gestures in your parish are meaningful to you?
    B. If you know any children, what symbols do they find meaningful?

5. Read Hebrews 8 and 9. According to Hebrews, the Ark symbolized realities of the New Testament. What, specifically, was symbolized by each of the following: Give short answers with scripture references.
    A. The high priest
    B. The sanctuary (also called the holy place or holy of holies)
    C. The sacrificial victims

Exercise   In order to get the flavor of the priestly author, reread the main Exodus passages by him: 1:1–5; 12:1–20; 24:16–18. Notice that he is particularly interested in genealogies and liturgical regulations, and that the phrase, "the glory of God," is characteristic of him.

Optional Challenge   1. Do a sketch, painting, or model of the Ark, the tent, of some object within them, or write a poem or prayer inspired by the Ark.

The idea of the holy place is pervasive in religion, and it is remarkable that early Israelite religion deviates from the common pattern. A holy object symbolizing the divine presence appears in the traditions earlier than the holy place and the holy building. . . . The holy object was the ark, called the ark of the covenant, the ark of the testimony, the ark of Yahweh or of elohim, and some similar titles. . . . This was a portable shrine symbolizing the presence of Yahweh; and such a portable shrine would be at home in a nomadic tribe which lives in tents, not houses. The ark was housed in a tent until the reign of David and then was permanently installed in the temple of Solomon.

— John L. McKenzie, A Theology of the Old Testament

SUGGESTIONS FOR THE STUDENT

After studying this lesson, you should:

1. Be able to identify the Tent of Meeting and the Ark of the Covenant and give a general description of them.

2. Be able to give the historical context for the Priestly author.

3. Be able to identify some major characteristics of the Priestly author. See "Sources of the Pentateuch," #6 in your SUPPLEMENTARY READINGS.

Memory Verse Suggestion:

Exodus 25:8 —   "And let them make me a sanctuary,
that I may dwell in their midst."

Other Exercises:

Review your grasp of the basic information so far by taking the Unit 1: Mid-Unit Self-Quiz, # 7 in your SUPPLEMENTARY READINGS.

Exodus 25:1–6   Contributions for sanctuary

I.7: The Golden Calf

Read: Exodus 24:12–18 and 32–34; Boadt, pp. 173–188; MDB: "Exodus, book of."

1. List the things you have learned about Joshua so far in Exodus.
    Give scripture references.

2. As you reflect on the prayers of Moses in these chapters, what do you learn that
    can be helpful in your own prayer?

3. What similarities do you see between Moses and Jesus? Be sure to use the scrip-
    ture text and not the MDB for this question.

4. Read Exodus 32:7–14. Whose people are the Israelites said to be?
    Give scripture references.

5. Some scholars think that Exodus 34:10–28 does not really describe a different
    event from that described in Exodus 19 and 20. They think that 34:1–28 is the J
    version of the Sinai covenant, which is described by P and E in Chapters 19 and
    20. Read both passages and decide whether you think they could be descrip-
    tions of the same event. Why or why not? (There is no right or wrong answer for
    this question. The aim of the question is to get you to read the scripture text
    carefully and to think about it.)

Exercise 1   Most scholars think that verses 7–11 of Chapter 33 were inserted from a different
                   source. Read Chapter 33 omitting verses 7–11. Then reread it including verses
                   7–11. Try to discover why scholars think these verses interrupt the flow of the story.
                   Note the different ideas in the two sources about the possibility of seeing God's
                   face.

Exercise 2   You will be responsible for one memory verse of your choosing from Exodus on the
                   quarter test. Be sure to include the chapter and verse numbers.

Optional   1. Describe Moses in one of these forms:
Challenge   A. A diary written by himself.
                       B. An article about him written by Joshua.
                       C. A work of art, poem, or song.

SUGGESTIONS FOR THE STUDENT

After studying this lesson, you should:

1. Be able to describe the story of the Golden Calf and its meaning.

2. Be able to give examples of the major characteristics of the Yahwist. See "Sources of the Pentateuch," #6 in your SUPPLEMENTARY READINGS.

3. Be able to describe the probable historical setting of the Yahwist.

Memory Verse Suggestion:

Exodus 34:6 —   "The Lord, The Lord,
a God merciful and gracious,
slow to anger,
and abounding in steadfast love
and faithfulness."

Exodus 32:19   Moses throws tablets down

I.8: Torah: The Law

Read: Leviticus 12–14, 16, 19, 23, 26; MDB: "Pentateuch"; Boadt, pp. 188–193.

1. A. Where in the New Testament is the ritual in Leviticus 12:6–8 carried out?
    B. In reading Leviticus 12:6–8, what do we learn about the New Testament event which we could not have known from the New Testament alone?

2. What New Testament passages do you understand better because of having read Leviticus 13 and 14?

3. Choose one of the days of special observance mentioned in Leviticus 23. If you were an Israelite priest responsible for giving a brief homily on this day, what would you say to make the people aware of the spiritual meaning of the ritual?

4. Find a New Testament reference to each feast on the chart below. (Hint: use footnotes, cross references and your MDB.)

Pilgrim Feasts	Hebrew Name	References	Historical Commemoration	Seasonal Celebration
Passover	Pesach	Ex 12 Lv 23:4–14 Dt 16:1–8	Deliverance from Egypt	First Sheaf of barley (Spring)
Pentecost (Weeks)	Shavuoth	Dt 16:9–12 Lv 23:15–21	Giving of Torah at Sinai	Grain Harvest (Summer)
Feast of Tabernacles (Booths)	Succoth	Neh 8 Lv 23:33–36 Dt 16:13–15	Wanderings in the wilderness	Grape Harvest (Autumn)

5. Look through the chapters of Leviticus you were NOT required to read until you find one passage that has significance today. Give the passage and the significance you find in it.

Optional Exercise   Read the articles in MDB on: Sabbath; Atonement, Day of; Pentecost; Tabernacles, feast of.

Optional Challenge

1. Give some contemporary examples of scapegoats. What is the relationship between the contemporary use of the word and its use in Leviticus 16:20–22?

2. Ask a Jewish friend what feasts are most significant for her/him, and how they are celebrated today.

SUGGESTIONS FOR THE STUDENT

After studying this lesson, you should:

1. Be able to name and briefly describe the three Pilgrim Feasts and the Day of Atonement.

2. See the connections between Levitical Law and Jesus' actions in the New Testament.

3. Be able to set Leviticus in its historical and literary context.

4. Be familiar with the spirituality of holiness in Leviticus.

Memory Verse Suggestion:

Leviticus 19:18 — "You shall love your neighbor as yourself. I am the Lord."

Israel's festivals were marked by the great rhythm of the Exodus, where hope and openness to the future were the distinguishing traits. In celebrating these feasts, Israel no longer celebrated the dying seasons but the living sacred history. It worshipped the eternal God who was guiding Israel to the time that had no end. The whole Israelite liturgy became simply a memorial of the Exodus.

— *Lucien Deiss,* God's Word and God's People

Leviticus 26:1–2   Worship of the golden idol

I.9: Forty Years of Wandering

Read: Numbers 6, 9–14, 16, 17, 20–24; MDB: "Miriam," "Balaam," "Serpent," "Water."
"The Genesis of Liberation: Moses Bound and Unbound," #8 in your SUPPLEMENTARY
READINGS.

1. A. What obligations did an Israelite take on by taking the Nazirite Vow?
    B. Do you know anyone in the New Testament who seems to have taken the
        Nazirite Vow?

2. What do we learn about the Passover in Chapter 9 of Numbers which we did
    not learn in Exodus?

3. A. Describe the mission of the twelve scouts.
    B. What was the nature of their report upon returning?

4. A. From what tribe was Korah?
    B. What was his reason for rebelling against Moses?
    C. From what tribe were Dathan and Abiram?
    D. What were their reasons for rebelling against Moses?

5. From which of the four sources do you think that Chapter 17 of Numbers came?
    Why? Be as specific as you can for your answer.

6. What message do you think the story of the 70 elders has for the church today?

7. What message for our lives do you find in the Balaam story?

Optional   1. Write a newspaper account of the scouts' trip and their report to the
Challenge   Israelite community.

2. Research and write a report on the land of Canaan and its inhabitants before the
    Israelites entered it.

3. Write a funeral oration that Moses might have given for either Aaron or Miriam.

4. The New Testament authors seem to have been familiar with these sections of
    Numbers. What connections can you discover between this material and that of:

    Matthew 2:1–12 ....Numbers 24:17

    John 3:14................................Numbers 21:6–9

    2 Peter 2:16 ....Numbers 22

    1 Corinthians 10:4 ....Numbers 20:2–13

SUGGESTIONS FOR THE STUDENT

After studying this lesson, you should:

1. Be able to identify the following: Nazirite Vow, Kadesh-Barnea, Meribah, Moab, Caleb, Korah, Dathan and Abiram, Balaam, Balak.

2. Be able to recognize the pattern of murmuring and lack of trust, followed by punishment, a cry for help and eventual relenting of Yahweh.

Memory Verse Suggestion:

Numbers 6:24–26 —   The Lord bless you and keep you.
                     The Lord let His face shine upon you,
                     and be gracious to you.
                     The Lord look upon you kindly,
                     and give you peace.

Having rejected safe slavery, Israel found its immediate destiny to be landlessness. But even in the wilderness it discovered that one may be a participant in one of two histories.... One is driven by a sense of banishment, characterized by mistrust expressed as quarrelsomeness and devoted to return to Egypt. The other is the history of hope, trusting in Yahweh's promises, enduring in the face of want and need, sure that history was on its way to the new and good land. Israel discovered what rootless people must each time learn over again, that in such landlessness there may be unexpected sustaining resources. Or one may discern there only darkness and abandonment. In the events of wilderness Israel wrestled like Jacob for its being and for its faith.

— Walter Brueggemann, The Land

Numbers 13:23 Carrying fruit from the Vale of Eschol

I.10: Guidesheet for Unit One Review

You will be responsible for:

1. The assigned readings in scripture, Boadt, the *Dictionary of the Bible*, and the SUPPLEMENTARY READINGS and other class handouts.

2. A memory verse from Exodus.

3. The proper spelling of the four traditions in the Pentateuch.

4. The characteristics of the Priestly, Yahwist, and the Elohist traditions. See "Sources of the Pentateuch," #6 in your SUPPLEMENTARY READINGS.

5. The following people, places, events, terms, etc.:

PEOPLE	PLACES	EVENTS	TERMS, ETC.
Aaron	Goshen	Pilgrim feasts	Ark of the Covenant
Amalekites	Horeb/Sinai	Passover	Covenant
Caleb	Kadesh Barnea	Pentecost	Covenant Code
Habiru	Marah	Tabernacles or Booths	Decalogue
Jethro	Midian	Golden calf incident	Holiness Code
Joshua	Nile	Crossing the Reed Sea	Israel's infidelity and
Levi	Raamses	Day of Atonement	murmuring
Miriam	Reed Sea	Burning bush incident	Manna
Moses		Theophany on Mt. Sinai	Pentateuch
Ramses II		Plagues	Purification
Zipporah			Nazirite Vow
Scouts			Scapegoat
Korah			
Dathan			
Abiram			
Balaam			

OVERVIEW OF YEAR ONE — UNIT TWO
Reflections on the Origins

Objectives   1. To become familiar with the style and theology of Deuteronomy.
2. To study the theology and literary form of the first eleven chapters of Genesis, with emphasis on the themes of creation and sin.
3. To study the patriarchal history and learn about the geographical and cultural background of the Fertile Crescent. To come to know Abraham, Sarah, and their family.

Textbooks   Primary text: The Bible
Other texts: John L. McKenzie   *Dictionary of the Bible* (cited as MDB)
Lawrence Boadt   *Reading the Old Testament*
Pauline Viviano   *Genesis* (Collegeville Bible Commentary)
Hammond's   *Atlas of Bible Lands*

Assignments   For each biblical passage, students should study the footnotes and the commentary for that particular passage.

II.1   A NEW FOCUS ON THE COVENANT ....Deuteronomy 1, 4–11

II.2   MOSES' LAST SERMON AND DEATH.....................................Deuteronomy 29–34

II.3   THE CREATION ....Genesis 1–2

II.4   THE FALL ....Genesis 3–5

II.5   NOAH, BABEL ....Genesis 6–11

II.6   ABRAHAM, COVENANT...Genesis 12–17

II.7   ABRAHAM, SODOM, ISAAC ....Genesis 18–23

II.8   ISAAC, ESAU, JACOB...Genesis 24–35

II.9   JOSEPH ....Genesis 37–50

II.10   UNIT REVIEW

II.1: A New Focus on the Covenant

Read: Deuteronomy 1, 4–11; Boadt, pp. 347–357.

1. What differences do you notice between the account of Sinai-Horeb in Exodus 19 and that in Deuteronomy 4:9-15?

2. Compare the Ten Commandments as they are given in Deuteronomy 5:6–21 with the commandments as they are given in Exodus 20:1–17. How are they similar and how do they differ?

3. List some verses from this portion of Deuteronomy that are particularly meaningful to you and briefly explain why you find them meaningful.

4. According to Moses, in what way is the Promised Land better than Egypt? (Dt 11:10-11)

5. The Deuteronomist had a great love for the law. How is this expressed in these chapters? Give specific examples, citing chapter and verse.

Optional Challenge

1. Do a work of art, poem, or song based upon some verse of Deuteronomy.

2. Deuteronomy emphasizes handing on the sacred stories to our children. Tell one of the stories from Exodus, Numbers, or Deuteronomy to a child. How did the child respond to the story?

3. What sections of scripture we have studied so far might you use if you were asked to prepare a prayer service for one of these: a child's birthday, an adult birthday, Thanksgiving, a retirement party, a gathering in a sick room, a parish council meeting, a graduation?

4. Ask a Jewish friend about phylacteries and mezuzah.

[Deuteronomy is] an eloquent and moving summons to a radical renewal based upon faith and a profound love for God and gratitude to God....It still calls us today, and it still retains its power and urgency.

— Claude Peifer, "The Book of Deuteronomy: A Blueprint for Renewal," in The Bible Today, *April 1977*

SUGGESTIONS FOR THE STUDENT

After studying this lesson, you should:

1. Know the historical and geographic background of Deuteronomy.

2. Know the characteristics of the Deuteronomic style. See "Sources of the Pentateuch," #6 in your SUPPLEMENTARY READINGS.

3. Know that Deuteronomy is written in the sermon form.

4. Know the Shema and its relationship to Judaism.

5. Know the significance for Jews of the phylacteries and mezuzah.

Memory Verse Suggestion:

Deuteronomy 6:4-5 —   "Hear, O Israel:
                        The Lord our God is one Lord;
                        and you shall love the Lord your God
                        with all your heart,
                        and with all your soul,
                        and with all your might."

Other Exercises:

Contact a Jewish synagogue in your area and join them for their Sabbath prayer or for one of their holiday liturgies.

Deuteronomy 6:4–5   "Hear, O Israel"

II.2: Moses' Last Sermon and Death

Read: Deuteronomy 29–34.

1. A. In what country are Moses and the Israelites when he gives this sermon?
   B. What other story have we studied that took place there?
   C. On what mountain in that country did Moses die?

2. How does the author of Deuteronomy, writing centuries after the death of Moses, show his readers that the Mosaic covenant does not belong only to the past, but also to them? Give references.

3. How is Deuteronomy 30:15-20 relevant for today? Be specific.

4. Choose one of the following: Either write a eulogy for Moses or write a final blessing which the dying Moses might have given to Joshua.

5. What is your favorite passage from Deuteronomy, Chapters 29-34? Why?

Exercise   Notice the frequency with which the ideas of "love" and "life" and the expression "With your whole heart and whole soul" appear in Chapter 30.

Optional   Read these other farewell discourses: Jacob, Genesis 49; Paul, Acts 20:17-33;
Exercise   Tobit, 14.

Optional   1. Compare the book of Deuteronomy to the farewell discourse of Jesus
Challenge   in John 14–17.

The Jordan looms as a decisive boundary in the Bible. It is not simply between east and west but is laden with symbolic power. It is the boundary between the precariousness of the wilderness and the confidence of at-home-ness. The crossing of the Jordan is the most momentous experience that could happen to Israel.... With good reason at that moment, Israel pauses to do what it does when it is most characteristically Israel—it listens!... And Moses, covenanter and shaper of Israel, speaks and in his speaking defines the shape and character of the new Israel, of Israel in the land and for the land and over the land. Thus the tradition of Deuteronomy is precisely placed at the moment of the Jordan, where characteristically Israel listens and Moses speaks. In that speaking/hearing moment, a new Israel is called into being, one appropriate for the new time of the land.

— Walter Brueggemann, The Land

SUGGESTIONS FOR THE STUDENT

After studying this lesson, you should:

1. Recognize that the covenant and the Word are living realities in Deuteronomy and in our lives also.

2. Notice the important Deuteronomic themes: Covenant, Life, Land, Law, Choice, and Love of God and for God.

3. Know the story of Moses' farewell address and death.

Memory Verse Suggestion:

Deuteronomy 30:14 —   "The word is very near you,
already in your mouth
and in your hearts.
You have only to carry it out."

Other Exercises:

The New Testament frequently quotes Deuteronomy. Look for passages in Deuteronomy which you also find in the New Testament.

Deuteronomy 34:1–4 Moses ascends Mt. Nebo

II.3: The Creation

Read: Genesis 1, 2; Boadt, Chapter 6, "The Preface to Israel's Story"; *Genesis* (Collegeville Bible Commentary), pp. 9-19. "Creation Myths from Other Cultures," #9 in your SUPPLEMENTARY READINGS.

1. According to Boadt, what was the intention of the authors of Genesis in writing the book? (*Summarize* in your own words.)

2. What differences does Boadt point out between the pagan myths and the biblical creation accounts?

3. Choose two of the "creation myths" found in #9 of your SUPPLEMENTARY READINGS. Answer this question about each of them separately.
   "What is the author of this myth trying to communicate about human life, the world, and/or God?" The message should be a *present reality*, not about a past event. Be sure your verbs are in the present tense. (Caution: Don't just retell the story. What does it tell you about life, our world, God?)

4. Answer the question in #3 about each of the biblical creation accounts:
   A. Genesis 1:1-2:4a (the Priestly creation account)
   B. Genesis 2:4b-25 (the Yahwist creation account)

Exercise   Be sure you know the names of the books of the Pentateuch, in order, and that you can spell them properly.

Optional   1. Answer the question given in #3 above about some other myth you know,
Challenge   or about another one of those found in the SUPPLEMENTARY READINGS.

2. Illustrate some part of this week's reading from scripture by a picture or poem.

The Bible is not an end but a beginning; a precedent, not a story — the perennial motion of the spirit. It is a book that cannot die, that is incapable of becoming stale or obsolete. Oblivion shuns its pages. Its power is not subsiding. In fact, it is still at the very beginning of its career, the full meaning of its content having hardly touched the threshold of our minds; like an ocean at the bottom of which countless pearls lie; waiting to be discovered, its spirit is still to be unfolded. Though its words seem plain and its idiom translucent, unnoticed meanings, undreamed intimations break forth constantly. More than two thousand years of reading and research have not succeeded in exploring its full meaning. Today it is as if it had never been touched, never been seen, as if we had not even begun to read it.

— Abraham Joshua Heschel, Israel

SUGGESTIONS FOR THE STUDENT

After studying this lesson, you should:

1. Understand the concept of myth from a biblical perspective.

2. Know there are two distinct creation stories, one Priestly and one Yahwist.

3. Recognize that the creation stories continue to have meaning in our lives.

4. Know that Chapters 1–11 of Genesis are called primitive or primeval history and their literary form is myth.

Memory Verse Suggestion:

Genesis 1:31 — "And God saw everything that he had made, and behold, it was very good."

Identifying the Literary Form Guides the Whole Interpretation

Once readers have determined the literary form of any biblical book or passage, standards applicable to that form help to clarify what the author meant, i.e., the literal sense. . . . Many past difficulties about the Bible have stemmed from the failure to recognize the diversity of literary forms that it contains and from the tendency to misinterpret as scientific history pieces of the Bible that are not historical or are historical only in a more popular sense. . . . If one correctly classifies a certain part of the Bible as fiction, one is not destroying the historicity of that section, for it never was history; one is simply recognizing the author's intention in writing that section. . . . Biblical fiction is just as inspired as biblical history.

— Rev. Raymond E. Brown, S.S., "Hermeneutics," New Jerome Biblical Commentary

Genesis 2:23 "Bone of my bone, flesh of my flesh."

II.4: The Fall

Read: Genesis 3–5; *Genesis* (Collegeville Bible Commentary), pp. 19–29; "The Yahwist Passages from the Pentateuch," #10 in your SUPPLEMENTARY READINGS.

1. What point in Chapter 3 shows that God continued to care for Adam and Eve even after their sin?

2. On the basis of your experience, do you think that the author of these chapters has a good understanding of human nature with regard to temptation and sin? Explain. Be specific.

3. A. What is the purpose of the mark God places on Cain?
   B. What does this suggest about God's attitude toward the sinner?
   C. About human beings' attitude toward the sinner?

4. A. From which of the four sources of the Pentateuch do you think 4:26b comes?
   B. Give your reason.

5. A. From which source of the Pentateuch do you think Chapter 5 comes? Why?
   B. What similarities do you notice with Chapter 1 which is from the same source?

6. What similarities do you see between the story of Cain and Abel and that of the Prodigal Son found in Luke 15:11–32?

Optional Challenge

1. In composing these stories, the author had in mind aspects of the world in which he lived. He composed the stories as a way of reflecting on these realities. What realities might they have been? Explain.

2. Compose a prayer or poem based on these chapters.

The way that leads out of the darkness is peace between brothers, care for our fellow humans. To care for our brother ardently, actively, is a way of worshipping God, a way of loving God. The clash between fathers and sons does not occupy much place in the Bible. Signs of the Oedipus complex rarely appear in the history of Israel. In the view of the Bible, the conflict which brings chaos down upon the world is hatred among brothers, fraternal hatred; the enmity between Cain and Abel, the tensions between Ishmael and Isaac, between Esau and Jacob. What were the happenings which poison the nation and the history of Israel? The selling of Joseph by his brothers, the disputes and clashes among the tribes, the enmity and division between Judah and Israel, between Jerusalem and Samaria.

— Abraham Joshua Heschel, Israel

SUGGESTIONS FOR THE STUDENT

After studying this lesson, you should:

1. Know the story line and main characters in the story of the fall and the story of Cain and Abel.

2. Recognize the theme of sin and its effects on humanity.

3. Recognize the theme of God's forgiveness.

Memory Verse Suggestion:

Genesis 4:7 — "If you do well, you can hold up your head:
but if not, sin is crouching at the door:
its urge is toward you,
yet you can be its master."

Genesis 3:1
"The snake — the most subtle of all animals."

II.5: Noah, Babel

Read: Genesis 6–11; *Genesis* (Collegeville Bible Commentary), pp. 30–43.

1. Genesis 3–11 is a presentation of human sin, and of God's loving care which brings hope in spite of the evils that come from sin. List four details of the stories that show God's loving care (e.g., 6:18–21, God instructs Noah about how he can be saved, even reminding him to bring food for himself and the animals in the ark). Give the chapter and verse numbers for each example.

2. What evidence do you find in Genesis 6:11–7:5 that more than one source was used in compiling the text? Do not name the source. Just *identify the evidence* which indicates that more than one source is present in the biblical text.

3. Christian tradition has seen the story of Pentecost in Acts 2 as a reversal of the story of Babel. Read Acts 2:1–13 carefully. Is there any sign that Luke might have had the story of Babel in mind as he wrote about Pentecost? Explain.

4. Compose a myth. Choose some present day reality and answer the question "How did this come to be?" First write down the specific present day reality on which you choose to reflect. Then express your reflections on *why* the reality exists. Write your reflections in the form of a story. Be sure your story explains how the reality came to be the way it is.

Optional   Read the MDB article on "myth."
Exercise

Optional   1. Research and write a report on the flood story in the Epic of Gilgamesh and
Challenge   compare and contrast it with the flood story in Genesis.

2. Present in a creative form — poem, play, picture, song, etc. — one of the biblical myths we have studied.

No matter how drastic human sin becomes, destroying what God has made good and bringing the world to the brink of uncreation, God's grace never fails to deliver humankind from the consequences of its sin. Even when humankind responds to a fresh start with the old pattern of sin, God's commitment to the world stands firm, and sinful humankind experiences the favor of God as well as righteous judgment.

— *David Clines,* The Theme of the Pentateuch

SUGGESTIONS FOR THE STUDENT

After studying this lesson, you should:

1. Know the basic outline of the story of the Flood and the Tower of Babel story.

2. Recognize the presence of different sources in the biblical story.

3. Have a deeper understanding of myth as a literary form.

Memory Verse Suggestion:

Genesis 9:16 —   "When the rainbow is in the clouds,
I will look upon it and I will
remember the everlasting covenant
between God and every living creature
of all flesh that is upon the earth."

Genesis 8:11   "...the dove came back"

II.6: Abraham, Covenant

Read: Genesis 11:27–17:27; *Genesis* (Collegeville Bible Commentary), pp. 5–8 and pp. 43–56; "Father Abraham, My Friend and Mentor," #11 in your SUPPLEMENTARY READINGS.

1. Make a map of the Bible lands. Trace the journey of Abraham as it is described in these chapters of scripture, naming the principal stops.

2. Read Romans 4 and briefly summarize in your own words the message St. Paul is drawing from the story of Abraham.

3. Read James 2:14–23 and briefly summarize in your own words the message that James is drawing from the story of Abraham. Do you think it contradicts the message in Romans 4? Explain.

4. Compare and contrast the covenant which the Lord made with Abraham in Genesis chapters 15 and 17 with the covenant at Sinai.

5. Choose one of the chapters from Genesis which you read for this assignment. What message do you think it has for Christians today?

6. Answer the following questions briefly, basing your answer upon the material in *Genesis* (Collegeville Bible Commentary).
   A. What is a saga?
   B. How are sagas used in Genesis?
   C. How does the use of mythological motifs in Genesis differ from the use of these motifs among Israel's Near Eastern neighbors?

Optional Challenge   In Chapter 14, Abram meets Melchizedek. Locate other references to Melchizedek in the Old and New Testament. What added significance does the author of Hebrews give to Melchizedek? In reference to what sacraments is he mentioned in the church today?

SUGGESTIONS FOR THE STUDENT

After studying this lesson, you should:

1. Know the geographic locations of the major stops on Abraham's journey.

2. Be familiar with the call, the covenant, and the promise made to Abraham and Sarah.

3. Be able to identify Abraham, Sarah, Hagar, Lot, and Melchizedek.

4. Appreciate Abraham as a person of faith.

Memory Verse Suggestion:

Genesis 12:2 —   "I will make you a great nation,
and I will bless you,
and make your name great
so that you will be a blessing."

*It is precisely because he did not know where he was going
that Abraham knew he was on the right path!*

— St. Gregory of Nyssa

Genesis 12:4   "So Abraham went as Yahweh told him."

II.7: Abraham, Sodom, Isaac

Read: Genesis 18–23; Boadt, Chapter 7, "The Patriarchs"; *Genesis* (Collegeville Bible Commentary), pp. 56–71. "On Burying Our Isaacs," #12 in your SUPPLEMENTARY READINGS.

1. Draw a diagram showing the relationships between: Terah, Abraham, Lot and his daughters, Haran, Sarah, Hagar, Ishmael, the Moabites, the Ammonites, Isaac. Use Genesis Chapters 11–23 in responding to this question.

2. It has been said that an important theme of Chapters 18 and 19 is hospitality, contrasted to its opposite. What examples of hospitality and inhospitality do you see in this story?

3. Read Hebrews 11:8–19. What belief does the author attribute to Abraham which does not appear in Genesis?

4. In what kind of situation in our personal lives does the story of the sacrifice of Isaac have a message for us? Can you give an example from your own life?

5. List *in order of importance (in your opinion)* ten events in Abraham's life. Cite the chapter and verse for each.

6. Imagine that you are either Sarah or Hagar. Write an account of the events in these chapters from your perspective. If you choose Hagar, focus on Chapters 16 and 21. For Sarah, use Chapters 12–23.

Exercise   Locate these places on a map, and be sure you know what events in Genesis 11–23 took place at each: Ur, Haran, Shechem, Bethel, the Negeb, Egypt, Sodom, Gomorrah, Zoar, Hebron, Salem (Jerusalem), Beersheba.

Optional   1. Compose a prayer Abraham might have prayed, or a letter he might have
Challenge   written to his brother Nahor. Specify at what point in his life he is composing it.

2. In Luke 17:32, Jesus tells his disciples, "Remember Lot's wife." What message might the story of Lot's wife have for us today?

SUGGESTIONS FOR THE STUDENT

After studying this lesson, you should:

1. Know the basic events which occur in the chapters you have read.

2. Be able to identify the following: Isaac, Ishmael, Lot and his family, Abraham's three guests, Sodom, Gomorrah, Hebron/Mamre, and Mt. Moriah.

3. Be able to describe Abraham as a person of faith.

Memory Verse Suggestion:

Genesis 21:2 —   He said, "Take your son, your only son Isaac, whom you love, and go to the land of Moriah, and offer him there as a burnt offering upon one of the mountains of which I shall tell you."

A Commentary on the Isaac-Abraham Story
by Harvena Richter

One often wonders
what Isaac pondered on those
long three days back from the
*   Mount of Moriah —*
whether he should tell his mother
that his father was going to kill him
(Sarah's only son),
that God had rescued him just in time,
just happened to be there —
might not have been near the Mount of Moriah at all.
And there'd have been boy-flesh,
not sheep-flesh roasting.
But doubtless he'd have been scared to tell
*   his mother,*
frightened
that Sarah might have scratched Abraham's eyes out,
and he'd have to lead his father around
the rest of his life —
blind as Isaac had been
bound on the altar.
As it was, it would be plenty painful
to meet his father's gaze,
to see in those fierce eyes
the knowledge he'd been expendable,
that he hadn't been worth more than a shekel,
or a sheep from his father's flock.
For a long while there'd be no direction
he could look,
no thought he could think
safely.

II.8: Isaac, Esau, Jacob

Read: Genesis 24–35; Boadt, Chapter 5, "The Pentateuch"; *Genesis* (Collegeville Bible Commentary), pp. 71–104.

1. A. Why do you think Abraham is so emphatic about Isaac not returning to Haran?
    B. What message might this have for us?

2. What nations are descended from the two children who struggled in Rebekah's womb? (The story is told to point to the later struggles between these two.)

3. A. What tribe, descended from Abraham and Keturah, later played a part in the Exodus? (Remember that names that appear to refer to individuals often actually refer to tribes or nations.)
    B. What important people in Exodus come from this tribe?

4   Abraham is remembered most of all for his faith. What characteristic of Jacob stands out most for you? Give references to support your choice.

5. Choose either A or B in writing your answer, and base it on Genesis 32:23–33. How does Jacob's wrestling with "some man" (God) come to be lived out:
    A. in the history of the nation Israel?
    B. in the reality of your own life?

6. List the stories in Genesis so far which show rivalries between brothers, or the mothers of brothers.

Exercise   Choose one short passage about Abraham from Genesis and memorize it.

Optional   1. List the events in Genesis 12–35 that occur in the following: Shechem, Bethel,
Challenge   Hebron-Mamre, Beersheba. Give biblical chapter and verse for each.

2. Write an essay on the role of women in the time of the Patriarchs based upon the material in Genesis 12–35. Be sure to give specific examples with chapter and verse to back up your conclusions.

SUGGESTIONS FOR THE STUDENT

After studying this lesson, you should:

1. Be familiar with the major events in this passage: marriage of Isaac and Rebekah, rivalry between Esau and Jacob, Jacob's dream at Bethel, his experience in Haran wrestling with an angel.

2. Be able to identify the following: Isaac, Rebekah, Laban, Esau, Jacob, Rachel, Leah, Bethel, and Haran.

Memory Verse Suggestion:

Genesis 32:28 —   Then he said, "Your name shall no more be called Jacob, but Israel, for you have striven with God and with men, and have prevailed."

At every turn these patriarchs, who are to be the fathers of a great nation which will inherit the land of Canaan, are threatened by difficulties which would seem to make it impossible for God to keep his word to them. And throughout each story in Genesis, it is this word of God which forms the dramatic background of the narrative.

— *Paul J. and Elizabeth Achtenmeier,* The Old Testament Roots of Our Faith

Genesis 32:26   "... wrestled with him until daybreak."

II.9: Joseph

Read: Genesis 37–50; Boadt, Chapter 4, "Literary Tools for Old Testament Study"; *Genesis* (Collegeville Bible Commentary), pp. 105–133.

1. A. Dreams play an important part in the Joseph narrative. List the people who had dreams, and *briefly* describe the meaning of each dream.
    B. List three other instances in scripture where God, or one of the angels, spoke to someone through a dream. Give the scripture citation for each. (See your MDB for help if you need it.)

2. A major theme of the Joseph narrative is God's providence.
    A. What is your definition of providence?
    B. Have you ever had an experience which appeared to be providential? Explain.

3. Read Matthew 1:3 and Genesis 38. Why do you think that the evangelist included Tamar in his listing of the ancestors of Jesus?

4. Choose an incident in the Joseph narrative which you think is significant. What relevance does the incident have for today?

5. What new or helpful information did you find in Chapter 4 of Boadt?

Optional Challenge

1. It is believed that Egypt was ruled by the Hyksos when the Israelites came to Egypt. Research and write a report on them.

2. It was believed among ancient people that in the "death-bed blessing" of a father the efficacy of the blessing itself, or curse as the case may be, was irrevocable and released a power which effectively determined the character and destiny of the recipient. The poem in Chapter 49 is Israel's death-bed blessing and/or curse. Give an interpretation for each of the eleven oracles dealing with the twelve tribes of Israel. (A commentary might be helpful.)

This narrator (of the Joseph story) is attentive to the mysterious ways of God's providence. The purposes of God are not wrought here by abrupt action or by intrusions, but by the ways of the world which seem to be natural and continuous. There is no appeal for faith or response, for the main point is that the ways of God are at work, regardless of human attitudes or actions.

— Walter Brueggemann, Genesis

SUGGESTIONS FOR THE STUDENT

After studying this lesson, you should:

1. Know the basic outline of the Joseph story.

2. Recognize the literary form and unity of the Joseph story.

3. Be able to recognize the following: Joseph, Jacob, Judah, Tamar, Goshen.

Memory Verse Suggestion:

Genesis 46:3 — Then God said [to Israel],
"I am God, the God of your father;
do not be afraid to go down to Egypt;
for I will there make of you a great nation."

Other Exercises:

Read "Biblical Heroes and Their Journeys of Faith," #13 in your SUPPLEMENTARY READINGS.

Genesis 45:3 "I am Joseph."

II.10: Guidesheet for Unit Two Review

You will be responsible for the following:

1. Books of the Bible read during the second unit: Deuteronomy and Genesis.

2. Reading assignments from the Collegeville Bible Commentary and from Boadt.

3. Your memory verse on Abraham. Be sure you know the chapter and verse number, as well as the translation used: *New American, Revised Standard Version* or *New Revised Standard Version, Jerusalem* or *New Jerusalem Bibles.*

4. The Yahwist, Elohist, Deuteronomist, and Priestly sources. Know their characteristics, be able to spell them and identify examples of each. See "Sources of the Pentateuch," #6 in your SUPPLEMENTARY READINGS.

5. The books of the Pentateuch, their spelling and proper order.

6. The following people, places and terms:

PEOPLE		PLACES	TERMS	
Adam	Esau	Babel	myth	*Divino Afflante*
Eve	Laban	Ur	oral tradition	*Spiritu*
Cain	Benjamin	Haran	saga	Masoretic text
Abel	Potiphar	Canaan	Epic of Gilgamesh	Septuagint
Noah	Judah	Mt. Nebo	Covenant—	Vulgate
Abram/Abraham	Tamar	Sinai/Horeb	in general and	Primeval or
Sarai/Sarah	Keturah	Sodom	with Noah,	Primitive History
Hagar	Abimelech	Gomorrah	Abraham	
Isaac	Josiah	Zoar	and at Sinai	
Rebekah		Hebron/Mamre	Patriarchs	
Ishmael		Bethel	Matriarchs	
Jacob/Israel		Salem	circumcision	
Joseph		Eden	Themes of Genesis:	
Moses		Egypt	Promise	
Rachel		Goshen	Blessing	
Leah		Machpelah	Fulfillment	
Melchizedek		Shechem	ziggurat	
Terah		Beersheba	Twelve Tribes of	
Lot			Israel	

AN OVERVIEW OF YEAR ONE — UNIT THREE
Taking, Governing, Losing the Land

Objectives
1. To learn the major geographical features of Palestine by using Hammond's Atlas in connection with the study of the Deuteronomic History.
2. To study charismatic leadership in connection with Judges.
3. To follow the development of kingship.
4. To understand the role of prophecy as seen in Nathan and Elijah.
5. To understand Canaanite religion in connection with Elijah.
6. To become familiar with the archaeology of Palestine.
7. To reinforce the general concepts of Old Testament chronology by frequent reference to a timeline.

Assignments   (To be studied in preparation for discussion at class)

III.1   THE CONQUEST ....Joshua 1–6; 23, 24

III.2   CHARISMATIC LEADERS:

         GIDEON, DEBORAH, SAMSON ....Judges 4–8; 13–16

III.3   KINGSHIP: SAMUEL AND SAUL...1 Samuel 1–15

III.4   SAUL AND DAVID ....1 Samuel 16–31; 2 Samuel 1

III.5   DAVID AND NATHAN ....2 Samuel 2–12

III.6   DAVID AND ABSALOM ....2 Samuel 13–20; 1 Kings 1–3

III.7   SOLOMON, THE DIVIDED KINGDOM,

         ELIJAH..1 Kings 8–12; 17–21; 2 Kings 1

III.8   ELISHA AND ATHALIAH..2 Kings 2–13

III.9   THE FALL OF THE NORTHERN AND

         SOUTHERN KINGDOMS...2 Kings 17–25

III.10   FINAL FIRST YEAR REVIEW

III.1: The Conquest

Read: Joshua 1–6; 23 and 24; "Yahweh: A Warrior God?" #14 in your SUPPLEMENTARY READINGS.

1. Find some passage from the Pentateuch which gives background for each of these passages:
    A. Joshua 1:1 (Joshua)   E. Joshua 5:12 (manna)
    B. Joshua 3:3 (Ark of the Covenant)   F. Joshua 8:33 (command of Moses)
    C. Joshua 5:2–9 (circumcision)   G. Joshua 24:9–11 (Balaam)
    D. Joshua 5:11 (Passover)   H. Joshua 24:32 (burial of Joseph)

2. According to the larger map on page 11 of Hammond's *Atlas of Bible Lands*:
    A. Which are the Transjordan tribes (i.e., those that were assigned land on the east side of the Jordan River)?
    B. Which tribes inherit these places?
        1) Shiloh
        2) Hebron
        3) Beersheba
        4) Hazor

3. The style, themes, and ideas of the Deuteronomic History (Joshua, Judges, 1 and 2 Samuel, and 1 and 2 Kings) are very similar to those in the Book of Deuteronomy. What words, phrases or ideas in Joshua 23 and 24 remind you of Deuteronomy? Be specific.

4. Imagine that you are Rahab in her old age, telling her grandchildren about her experience with the Israelite invasion. What would you say?

Exercise   Read the last chapter of Deuteronomy and the first chapter of Joshua, noticing how the books form a continuous story. This illustrates why scholars link the historical books, beginning with Joshua, with Deuteronomy.

Optional   1. Describe the spirituality of Joshua as you understand it. Please give references.
Challenge
               2. Present Joshua in some creative form, e.g. drawing, poem, prayer.

               3. In Chapter 24, Joshua presides at a Covenant Renewal ceremony at Shechem. Research and write a report on the importance of Covenant Renewal ceremonies among the Israelites after they came into the Promised Land.

               4. Scholars have developed several theories regarding the conquest of Canaan by the Israelites. Research and report upon these theories.

SUGGESTIONS FOR THE STUDENT

After studying this lesson, you should:

1. Be able to identify Joshua and the Covenant Renewal at Shechem.

2. Be able to locate on a map: the Jordan River, Transjordan area, Jericho, and Shechem.

3. Know the books in the Deuteronomic History and when the final edition of the history was completed.

4. Recognize the importance of covenant fidelity as a Deuteronomic theme.

Memory Verse Suggestion:

Joshua 1:9 —   "Be strong and of good courage;
                be not frightened,
                neither be dismayed;
                for the Lord your God is with you
                wherever you go."

Other Exercises:

— Trace on a map the entrance into the land as it is described in Joshua.

Joshua 2:15 Joshua's men helped by Rahab

III.2: Charismatic Leaders: Gideon, Deborah, Samson

Read: Judges 4–8; 13–16; Boadt, Chapter 10, "The Israelites' Possession of Canaan; the Books of Joshua and Judges"; Sr. Macrina Scott, "Heroic Women of the Bible," # 15 in your SUPPLEMENTARY READINGS.

1. Give examples from Chapters 4 and 6 of the Deuteronomic pattern:
    — Israel sins
    — God punishes
    — Israel repents/cries to the Lord
    — God sends a deliverer
    Give the chapter and verse numbers for each example.

2. A. List *all* the women mentioned in the chapters of Judges you have read.
    B. What *general* insights do you get from them and their experience about the role of women in Israel at the time of the judges?

3. Choose one of the judges we have studied and write a character sketch of her or him. Be sure it is a *character sketch* of the individual and not just a physical description or a list of all the things the person said or did.

4. What similarities do you see between Judges 6:11–16 and Luke 1:26–38?

5. What similarities do you see between Judges 13:2–5 and Luke 1:5–25?

Exercise   On the maps on pages 11 and 12 in your Atlas, locate the following:
A. Deborah's palm tree—Judges 4:5
B. The home of Barak—Judges 4:6
C. Battle between Barak and Sisera—Judges 4:13–16 (Valley of Jezreel, Esdraelon)
D. The tribes that followed Gideon and the Midianites — Judges 6:35 and 7:23–25
E. Midianite camp which Gideon attacked—Judges 6:33
F. The place of Samson's imprisonment—Judges 16:21

Optional Challenges

1. Briefly discuss the main difference between Joshua 1–12 and Judges 1:1–2:5.

2. Briefly discuss the concept of the judge as a "charismatic leader." Use the MDB article "Judges." Give examples of modern "charismatic leaders."

SUGGESTIONS FOR THE STUDENT

After studying this lesson, you should:

1. Be able to identify: the charismatic leaders Gideon, Deborah, and Samson, role of the judges in Israel, who/what they were.

2. Be able to locate on the map: Mt. Tabor, the Jezreel Valley.

3. Understand the tribal federation under the judges.

4. Know the Deuteronomic pattern found in Judges:
    1. Israel sins
    2. God punishes
    3. Israel repents and cries for help
    4. God sends a deliverer.

Memory Verse Suggestion:

> Judges 5:3 —   "Hear, O kings, give ear, O princes;
> to the Lord I will sing,
> I will make melody to the Lord,
> The God of Israel."

From "Reflections on Deborah"

In the days of your prophet Deborah
You saved Israel by the hand of a woman.
In quiet wisdom she stood beneath her tree
guiding the searching ones in your Law.
She saw the threat of tyranny to her
*   simple people.*
She came to you for help and you
*   answered her.*

— Ann Johnson, Miryam of Nazareth

Judges 4:1   "Deborah . . . judging Israel . . ."

III.3: Kingship: Samuel and Saul

Read: 1 Samuel 1–15; Boadt, Chapter 12, "A King Like Those of Other Nations."

1. What passage in Numbers helps in understanding 1 Samuel 1:11?

2. What similarities do you see between Hannah and Mary?

3. What passage in Luke's gospel about the childhood of Jesus are you reminded of by 1 Samuel 2:26?

4. Why did the people want a king? Give scripture references to support your answer.

5. Give one passage from these chapters which seems to have a message for you. Explain why.

Exercise   Locate on the large map on p. 12 of Hammond's Atlas:
     A. the home of Elkanah—1 Samuel 1:1,19 (NT Arimathea, modern Rentis)
     B. Shiloh—1 Samuel 1:3 (modern Seilun)
     C. Aphek—1 Samuel 4
     D. Ashdod—1 Samuel 5:1
     E. Gaza, Ashkelon—1 Samuel 6:17
     F. Kiriath-Jearim—1 Samuel 7:1 (modern Abu Gosh)

Optional Challenge

1. Write an autobiography of Samuel, emphasizing his feelings as he looks back over the events of his life.

2. Research and write a report on the Philistines and their role in the Bible.

God remains, as He must in this unique theocratic kingdom, the only true king of Israel. Israel will have her human king as well, but he is not to be like the kings of the nations. He is to be a representative of God, the true King. He is to be the instrument through which God will work out the ultimate destiny of Israel. He must, therefore, be subject to the Mosaic law and to the admonitions and guidance of God's prophets.

— Peter F. Ellis, C.SS.R., The Men and the Message of the Old Testament

SUGGESTIONS FOR THE STUDENT

After studying this lesson, you should:

1. Be able to identify: Eli, Hannah, Samuel, and Saul.

2. Be able to describe the tension surrounding the move from tribal federation to monarchy.

Memory Verse Suggestion:

1 Samuel 3:10 — And the Lord came and stood forth,
calling as at other times, "Samuel! Samuel!"
And Samuel said, "Speak, for thy servant hears."

Other Exercises:

There are many fictional works based upon the people and the times described in the Deuteronomic History. Among these are:
The Scarlet Cord, by Frank Slaughter (Rahab)
Gideon, by Paddy Chayefsky (a play)
Eyeless in Gaza, by Aldous Huxley (Samson)
The Samson Riddle, by Wolf Mankowitz
The Source, by James Michener (very good on all biblical periods)
The Golden City, by Peter Dickinson (excellent versions of the biblical stories as they might have been told orally before being written down)

1 Samuel 3:10   "Speak, Yahweh . . . your servant is listening."

III.4: Saul and David

Read: 1 Samuel 16–31; 2 Samuel 1; Boadt, Chapter 3, "Archaeology and the Old Testament."

1. After reading the assigned chapter on Boadt, explain briefly how archaeology has contributed to our understanding of the Old Testament.

2. Write a character sketch (*not a physical description or list of events*) of David as he appears in the scripture assigned this week. Give references for each statement.

3. A. Choose an incident in these chapters which you think is significant.
    B. What message for your own life do you find in this incident?

4. Imagine that you are a newspaper reporter, assigned to write a story with one of the following titles:
    1. King Saul Dies a Hero's Death
    2. Man Executed Who Boasted He Slew King
    3. Jonathan Played Secret Role in David's Escape from Saul

Exercise   Locate the following places on the map on p. 12 of the Atlas: Bethlehem, Socoh, Ramah, Gath, Gibeah. Be sure that you know what event occurred in each place.

Optional Challenge

1. Describe Saul as he appears in each of these sections of the story:
    a) David at court (1 Sm 16:1–19:7)
    b) The flight of David (1 Sm 19:8–21:16)
    c) David the outlaw (1 Sm 22:1–26:25)
    d) David among the Philistines (1 Sm 27:1–2 Sm 1:27)

2. Write a eulogy David might have given at Saul's funeral.

3. Express your feelings about some part of these chapters in the form of a picture or poem.

4. Assume that you are David applying for the job as King of Israel. Write a resume.

What is it that makes David endlessly fascinating to us?... On the one hand, David is much like us. There is something genuinely human about him, which means that there is a shape to his life that we can count on and identify with. There is also a freedom about him that makes him interesting and not boring. But even while we are able to identify with him, there is a distance between David and us. That distance is because of his nerve and grandeur in which he can make the great gesture that carries everyone before him.... There is, then, the ability to identify with and yet to be called out beyond ourselves, for we know we are in the presence of greatness.

                                        — *Walter Brueggemann*, David's Truth in Israel's Imagination and Memory

SUGGESTIONS FOR THE STUDENT

After studying this lesson, you should:

1. Know how the work of biblical archaeologists enriches our study of scripture by giving the text a "cultural context."

2. Be able to identify: Saul, Jonathan, Goliath, Michal, Abner, Joab, and Abigail.

Memory Verse Suggestion:

1 Samuel 16:7 — "God does not see as human beings see;
　　　　　　　they look at appearances
　　　　　　　but God looks at the heart."

Other Exercises:

There have been many books, plays, and movies about the life of David.
Some which you might want to read are:

— *David of Jerusalem*, a novel by Louis de Wohl

— *The King David Report,* a novel by Stefan Heyme which illustrates the way in which the biblical text about David was shaped by the politics of writers and editors

— "David and Jonathan," a play by D. H. Lawrence

1 Samuel 16:23
"David would take a harp and play."

III.5: David and Nathan

Read: 2 Samuel 2–12; Boadt, Chapter 13, "Daily Life in Ancient Israel."

1. What reasons do you think David may have had for choosing these cities as his capitals?
    A. Hebron (Remember the passages you read earlier this year about Hebron)
    B. Jerusalem

2. List the *principal* passages about the Ark of the Covenant you have studied since the beginning of the year.

3. List the promises given in the oracle of Nathan (Chapter 7) putting them *into your own words*.

4. Write a character sketch of one of the following, giving references:
    Abner, Joab, Ishbaal, Michal.

5. What do you learn about the character of David from these chapters in addition to what you learned in previous chapters?

6. Based upon your reading in Chapter 13 of Boadt, describe several ways in which the lifestyle or beliefs in ancient Israel differed from ours in significant ways.

Exercises   A. Notice how often "forever" or similar expressions are used in the prayer David prayed after receiving Nathan's oracle.
                B. Locate on the map on p. 13 of the Atlas the conquests of David mentioned in 2 Samuel 8:1–14.

Optional   1. Write a poem or produce some other work of art based upon these chapters
Challenge   of scripture.

2 Samuel 6:14   "...and David danced..."

SUGGESTIONS FOR THE STUDENT

After studying this lesson, you should:

1. Know the significance of the Davidic covenant.

2. To be able to identify: Jesse, David, Nathan, Bathsheba, Michal, Abner, Joab, Ish-baal, and Uriah the Hittite.

3. To be able to locate Hebron and Jerusalem on a map.

Memory Verse Suggestion:

2 Samuel 7:22 – [David said] "Therefore thou art great, O Lord God;
for there is none like thee,
and there is no God besides thee,
according to all we have heard in our ears."

and david danced

sing david,
    dance david,
        make the mountains ring!
        dance david,
            sing david,
                before the LORD your King!
            now in abandon, spin!!
            lead those you have led
        through the streets of zion.
    strike your harp,
make the walls resound!
    shout with joy, leap! like a boy.
        whirl in ecstacy, toss your locks,
            never mind those who mock!
            let love pour, let it pour,
                with open heart, pour some more
                    praise the LORD forevermore!
                sing david,
            dance david,
        make the mountains ring!
        dance david,
    sing david,
before the LORD, your King!

— *Mary E. Ingenthron, Catholic Biblical School Graduate '86, in*
The Bible Today, *September 1984*

III.6: David and Absalom

Read: 2 Samuel 13–20; 1 Kings 1–3.

1. Why do you think Absalom chose Hebron as a place to be proclaimed king?

2. What do you think of David as a father? Give references.

3. What contemporary lessons do you find in these chapters?

4. Write a list of questions and answers from 2 Samuel which you think would be suitable for a test. (This could be matching columns, multiple choice, a crossword puzzle, or anything that strikes your fancy.) Be sure to include your answers.

5. Write a eulogy for David's funeral.

Exercises   A. Locate on the map on p. 13 of the Atlas the cities traditionally named as the limits of David's kingdom, Dan and Beersheba.
                       B. Which of these places were conquered by David? Ezion-geber (modern Elat), Rabbah, Ammon (modern Amman), Damascus, Hazor, Ashkelon, Acco, Tyre, Bethel, Jericho.

Optional   1. Read 2 Samuel 14:1–24 and 2 Samuel 20:14–22. What picture do you get of the
Challenge   role of the wise woman in Israel?

2. Read 2 Samuel 16:20–23, 2 Samuel 3:6–7 and 1 Kings 2:13–25. What do you learn from these passages about concubines?

2 Samuel 19:1   "Absalom, O my son Absalom"

SUGGESTIONS FOR THE STUDENT

After studying this lesson, you should:

1. Be able to identify: Amnon, Absalom, Tamar, Adonijah, Solomon, and Zadok.

2. Be able to describe the succession narrative, its probable origin and purpose.

3. Be able to list David's major accomplishments as king.

Memory Verse Suggestion:

1 Kings 3:9 — [Solomon said] "Give thy servant therefore
an understanding mind to govern thy people,
that I may discern between good and evil;
for who is able to govern this thy great people?"

Other Exercises:

Review the Deuteronomic History with the Self-Quiz, #16 in your SUPPLEMENTARY READINGS.

CAST OF MAJOR CHARACTERS

Samuel		Saul		David	
Elkanah	(father)	Kish	(father)	Jesse	(father)
Hannah	(mother)	Jonathan	(eldest son)	Jonathan	(friend)
Eli	(priest of Shiloh)	Michal	(daughter)	Michal	(wife)
		Abner	(general)	Joab	(nephew and general)
		Ishbaal	(son)	Abigail	(wife)
			(also called Ishbosheth)	Abiathar	(only surviving priest of Nob: descendant of Eli)
		Meribaal	(also called Mephibosheth — lame son of Jonathan)	Nathan	(prophet)
				Bathsheba	(wife)
				Amnon	(first son by Ahinoam)
				Absalom	(son by Maacah)
				Tamar	(daughter by Maacah)
				Adonijah	(son by Haggith)
				Solomon	(son by Bathsheba)
				Zadok	(priest with Abiathar; anointed Solomon; became chief priest when Abiathar was deposed for supporting Adonijah's rebellion)

III.7: Solomon, The Divided Kingdom, Elijah

Read: 1 Kings 8–12; 17–21; 2 Kings 1; MDB: "The Temple"; Boadt, Chapter 11, "Canaanite Religion and Culture"; "Elijah: Zealous for the Lord," #17 in your SUPPLEMENTARY READINGS.

1. Using the time chart at the back of Hammond's Atlas, pp. 40–42, answer these questions:
   A. What monuments would Abraham have seen on his visit to Egypt if he went to Gizeh?
   B. Which law code came first, the Ten Commandments or the Law of Hammurabi?
   C. What prophets lived around the time that legend says Rome was founded?
   D. What prophets had been active before Josiah's reform?
   E. What king reigned in Judah at about the time of Homer?

2. Mention some facts about each of these which would be important to you if you were considering whether to vote for or against them for public office:
   A. David   B. Solomon   C. Rehoboam

3. What events had made Shechem and Penuel sacred and therefore suitable for Jeroboam's capital?

4. Luke thinks of Jesus as a prophet like Elijah. What passage about Elijah is he thinking of as he writes: Luke 4:25–26, Luke 7:11–17, Luke 9:61–62?

5. List ten characters from the Deuteronomic History whom you want to remember with brief (5–10 words) descriptions of each.

6. State at least one thing which you learned from the chapter in Boadt which helped you to understand the scripture text more fully.

Exercise   On the map on page 13 of the Atlas locate the following:
A. Ezion-geber where Solomon built a fleet of ships for international trade.
B. Tyre, from whose king, Hiram, Solomon purchased cedar wood.
C. Dan and Bethel where Jeroboam set up the golden calves for the Israelites' worship at the northern and southern limits of Israel.
D. Mt. Carmel where Elijah confronted the priests of Baal.

Optional Challenge

1. Write a character sketch or poem about Elijah, or draw a picture of him.

2. Draw Solomon's Temple, or some part of it.

SUGGESTIONS FOR THE STUDENT

After studying this lesson, you should:

1.   Be able to identify: Solomon, Queen of Sheba, Rehoboam, Jeroboam I, Elijah, Ahab and Jezebel, Baal, the Widow of Zarephath, and Naboth.

2.   Be able to describe the division of the kingdom into Israel in the north and Judah in the south.

Memory Verse Suggestion:

1 Kings 19:11b–12 —   "And behold, the Lord passed by,
and a great strong wind rent the mountains,
and broke in pieces the rocks before the Lord,
but the Lord was not in the wind;
and after the wind an earthquake,
but the Lord was not in the earthquake;
and after the earthquake a fire,
but the Lord was not in the fire;
and after the fire a still small voice."

At Sunday school, the topic was Elijah and the prophets of Baal. The teacher explained that Elijah built an altar, placed wood on it, cut the sacrificial bullock in pieces and laid them on the wood. He then commanded that the people fill four jars of water and pour the water over the sacrifice. "Why do you think they did that?" asked the teacher. A little girl raised her hand and said, "To make gravy."

— Taken from Reader's Digest, *June, 1986*

1 Kings 10:1–2   The Queen of Sheba visits Solomon

III.8: Elisha and Athaliah

Read: 2 Kings 2–13; Boadt, Chapter 15, "The Kingdom Split in Two."

1. Elijah and Elisha were well known to Jesus and the authors of the New Testament.
   A. What similarities do you notice between 2 Kings 4:42–44 and John 6:5–15?
   B. Read Matthew 3:1–12, 11:7–15 and 17:9–13. What similarities do you see between Elijah and John the Baptist?

2. List three events we have studied this year which occurred at the Jordan River. (You may use events from this week's lesson.)

3. A. Using your lecture notes and Chapter 15 in Boadt, describe the biblical meaning of prophecy.
   B. Compare and contrast the early or former prophets and the later classical or writing prophets. (How are they similar and how do they differ from one another?)

4. Who are the prophets in our contemporary world (20th century)? Why do you think they are prophets?

Optional Challenge

1. What impressions do you get in these chapters of the relationship between the kings, the prophets, and the priests? Give references.

2. What do you learn from these chapters about communities of prophets? Give references. (It is probably in these communities that the stories of Elijah and Elisha were preserved.)

3. Create a timeline that will be useful to you in the study of the Old Testament.

CAST OF MAJOR CHARACTERS

Elisha	Prophet in Israel, follower of Elijah
Naaman	Syrian general cured of leprosy by Elisha
Athaliah	Member of the family of Ahab; wife of Jehoram of Juda; queen mother of Ahaziah of Judah. She ruled after the death of Ahaziah, favored Baal over Yahweh.
Jehoash (also called Joash)	The one son of Ahaziah who was rescued by his aunt and her husband the high priest from Athaliah's slaughter of her grandchildren. Ruled in Judah for 40 years and was faithful to Yahweh. Not to be confused with Jehoash, king of Israel.

SUGGESTIONS FOR THE STUDENT

After studying this lesson, you should:

1. Be able to identify: Elisha, Naaman, Shunamite woman, Athaliah.

2. Be able to distinguish between early or former prophets and the writing or classical prophets.

3. Know the role of the prophet in Israel.

Memory Verse Suggestion:

2 Kings 2:11 — "And as they still went on and talked, behold,
a chariot of fire and horses of fire
separated the two of them.
And Elijah went up by a whirlwind into heaven."

2 Kings 2:11 Elijah to heaven in whirlwind

III.9: The Fall of the Northern and Southern Kingdoms

Read: 2 Kings 17–25; Boadt, pp. 374–381, "Deuteronomist's History."

1. A. What motivated the Assyrians to invade Israel?
    B. According to the Deuteronomic Historian, for what sins of Israel did God
        allow them to be destroyed by the Assyrians?
    C. Can you think of any comparable sins today?

2. What is the origin of the Samaritans as described by the Deuteronomic Historian?

3. A. Describe the reform of Josiah.
    B. Has anything occurred in the church in this century that has some similarity
        to the reform of Josiah? What is the similarity?

4. Pretend that you are living in Jerusalem at the time of its destruction and the
    exile. Write a letter to a friend describing your experiences and your feelings
    about the events that took place.

5. According to Boadt:
    A. When was the Deuteronomic History written?
    B. What was the purpose of the Deuteronomic History?

Exercise   Be sure that you can locate the following on a map:
Damascus, Tyre, Mediterranean Sea (Great Sea), Dan, Jordan, Dead Sea, Jericho,
Jerusalem, Bethlehem, Hebron, Beersheba, Sea of Chinnereth (modern Sea of
Galilee), Moab.

Optional   1. Find examples in these chapters of the Deuteronomic Historian's concern
Challenge   with: reward and punishment; the land; prophecy; the covenant and obedience
                  to the law.

2. List the passages that indicate that the real international power struggle of the
    fertile crescent was between Egypt and Assyria or Babylon. Israel and Judah
    were tiny nations caught in the middle of great conflicts. Look on a map to see
    why this was so.

*But today there is no longer any nation for them. All the institutions that had framed and sustained the people have col-
lapsed, even the most sacred. There are no longer any kings, leaders, or priests. Can one still speak of them as a people? It
has been scattered to the four corners of the immense Chaldean empire. They are only men and women left to the forces
of their own hearts. Today it is up to each one of them to hear and to respond. The son no longer responds for the father
nor the father for the son. It is up to each one to choose: life or death.*

                                                        — Eloi Leclerc, O.F.M., People of God in the Night

SUGGESTIONS FOR THE STUDENT

After studying this lesson, you should:

1. Be able to identify: Hezekiah, Josiah, Assyrians, Babylonians, Isaiah, Jeremiah, Josiah's reform, Babylonian Exile, Jehoiakim, Zedekiah.

2. Be able to describe the fall of both the northern and southern kingdoms and know the Deuteronomic interpretation of these events.

Memory Verse Suggestion:

2 Kings 18:5 —   "He [Hezekiah] trusted in the Lord the God of Israel;
so that there was none like him
among all the kings of Judah after him,
nor among those who were before him."

CAST OF CHARACTERS

Hezekiah: King of Judah; faithful to Yahweh; prayed for protection from the Assyrians and was answered

Isaiah: Prophet who promised Hezekiah God's protection from the Assyrians and cured him when he was sick.

Sennacherib: King of Assyria who besieged Jerusalem, but was defeated by the plague when Hezekiah prayed.

Josiah: Grandson of Manasseh and king of Judah; after the discovery of the Book of the Law he gathered the people for a renewal of the covenant.

Nebuchadnezzar: King of Babylon (also called Chaldea) who conquered Judah.

Zedekiah: Last king of Judah who was appointed by the king of Babylon, but later rebelled against him, precipitating the destruction of Jerusalem.

The Destruction of Jerusalem

III.10: Guidesheet for Final First Year Review

For your exam, please know the following:

1. The books of the Pentateuch, their spelling and proper order.

2. The books in the Deuteronomic History, their spelling and proper order.
    Also know the basic theology of the Deuteronomic Historian.

3. The four sources of the Pentateuch, their spelling and some of their typical characteristics.

4. Know the chronology of the history we have studied so far. It is not important to know dates, but know the order in which the major characters and events occur (e.g., Elijah comes after Nathan but before Elisha).

5. Know and be able to locate the following on a map: Dan, Beersheba, Hebron, Jericho, Bethel, Shiloh, Shechem, Samaria, Jerusalem, Bethlehem, Jordan River, Dead Sea, Mediterranean Sea, Sea of Galilee (Chinnereth), Northern Kingdom (Israel), Southern Kingdom (Judah).

6. The following people and terms:

PEOPLE			TERMS	
Abraham	David	Rehoboam	Archaeology	Fall of the
Isaac	Goliath	Jeroboam I	Tell	Northern
Jacob	Jonathan	Elijah	Patriarchs/	Kingdom
Joseph	Michal	Ahab	Matriarchs	to Assyria
Moses	Abner	Jezebel	Invasion of	Destruction of
Miriam	Joab	Widow of	Canaan	Jerusalem
Aaron	Abigail	Zarephath	Covenant	Babylonian
Joshua	Nathan	Elisha	renewal	Exile
Rahab	Bathsheba	Shunammite	ceremony	Baal
Deborah	Uriah	woman	Promised Land	Solomon's
Barak	Ishbaal	Athaliah	Judges	Temple
Jael	Tamar	Naaman	Monarchy	Ark of the
Gideon	Amnon	Hezekiah	Davidic	Covenant
Samson	Absolom	Isaiah	Covenant	
Philistines	Adonijah	Josiah		
Delilah	Meribaal	Hilkiah		
Hannah	Shimei	Jeremiah		
Eli	Solomon	Jehoiachin		
Samuel	Queen of	Zedekiah		
Saul	Sheba			
Jesse	Hiram			

SUPPLEMENTARY READINGS

In this section you will find the readings suggested for use with the assignment questions. The index below identifies the reading and the assignment for which it is used.

1. MORE ABOUT BIBLE TRANSLATIONS..Introduction

2. A POPULAR GUIDE TO READING THE BIBLE....................................Introduction

3. THE DELIVERANCE AT THE SEA...I.3

4. THE DESERT: A ROUNDABOUT WAY..I.5

5. WHY IS THE BIBLE LIKE A CAMEL?...I.6

6. THE SOURCES OF THE PENTATEUCH..I.6

7. UNIT 1: MID-UNIT SELF-QUIZ...I.6

8. THE GENESIS OF LIBERATION:
    MOSES BOUND AND UNBOUND I.9

9. CREATION MYTHS FROM OTHER CULTURES II.3

10. THE YAHWIST PASSAGES FROM THE PENTATEUCH...............................II.4

11. FATHER ABRAHAM, MY FRIEND AND MENTOR.......................................II.6

12. ON BURYING OUR ISAACS..II.7

13. BIBLICAL HEROES AND THEIR JOURNEYS OF FAITH...............................II.9

14. YAHWEH: A WARRIOR GOD?..III.1

15. HEROIC WOMEN OF BIBLE..III.2

16. SELF-QUIZ: THE DEUTERONOMIC HISTORY III.6

17. ELIJAH: ZEALOUS FOR THE LORD...III.7

18. THE FOUR-YEAR STUDY PLAN OF THE CATHOLIC BIBLICAL SCHOOL

1. MORE ABOUT BIBLE TRANSLATIONS

For the serious Bible student, the first step is to acquire a good translation. Bible translations come in a dizzying variety not only of bindings, sizes and costs, but also in styles of translation. Some try to be very exact, while others paraphrase the author's meaning but not the exact words. Others digest some passages and eliminate others. Many Bibles provide helpful notes to aid the reader while others have no notes at all. The best study Bible is one which strives for accuracy and provides helpful notes to decipher the hard passages. For our students, three translations are highly recommended.

The *New American Bible* (NAB)

This 1970 translation from the original Hebrew and Greek was done by members of the Catholic Biblical Association of America under the sponsorship of the U.S. Bishops. It is the translation used for the Catholic lectionary readings at Mass. It contains brief introductions to each book as well as excellent footnotes and cross references to other biblical passages. In 1986 the New Testament section was thoroughly revised. The New Testament notes were updated and expanded to provide greater help for the reader. Some attempt has been made to include more inclusive language, but this aspect still demands further work. This translation is included in the *Oxford Catholic Study Bible* (1990) together with helpful reading guides for every book of the Bible.

The *Jerusalem Bible* (JB) or
The *New Jerusalem Bible* (NJB)

This Catholic version was first translated into English in 1966 from the French. It has excellent introductions, notes, and commentaries. The whole translation was revised and published in 1985. All the notes and introductory material were extensively updated. Since the translation was done primarily by British scholars, sometimes the word choice is more British than American. (Students should be careful not to get the Reader's Edition which does not contain the notes.)

The *Revised Standard Version* (RSV) or
The *New Revised Standard Version* (NRSV)
(OXFORD ANNOTATED WITH THE APOCRYPHA)

This is still one of the best modern translations because of its accuracy; however, the notes are not as extensive as the NAB or JB. Make sure that you get this with the notes and with the "Apocrypha," i.e., other ancient books of which seven are included in Catholic versions (called the Deuterocanonical Books) but not usually found in most Protestant Bibles. This translation was newly revised in 1990 and is called the *New Revised Standard Version*.

Not Recommended for Study

There are many other translations to choose from. However, many of these are not really suitable for serious Bible study. In particular, students should be careful when using such popular translations as the *Good News Bible*, which is very readable but often at the cost of gliding over difficult passages — it often gives what is considered the author's message more than the actual words. Another translation to be avoided is *The Living Bible* (the New Testament is called *The Way*) which is not a real translation but just a paraphrase. These Bibles, although very readable, do not help the serious student grapple with what the original author said. The *King James Bible* or the *Douay-Rheims* or *Confraternity* Catholic versions are really unsuitable for a modern student. Not only is their language archaic, but modern scholars produce far better and more accurate translations and notes than were possible when these were produced.

Other Translations

There are also various translations by groups, e.g., the *New English Bible* or the *New International Version*, and others by single individuals, e.g. Knox, Goodspeed (*The Chicago Bible*), and Phillips for the New Testament. These are interesting to read and can be very helpful for comparing how passages from the ancient Greek or Hebrew might be translated into English.

REMEMBER: Since no two languages express their understanding of reality in exactly the same way, *every translation is an interpretation of what the translator perceives the meaning of the scripture passage to be.*

Get your facts first,
and then you can distort them
as much as you please.

— Mark Twain

2. A POPULAR GUIDE TO READING THE BIBLE

By Sr. Macrina Scott, O.S.F.

Catholics today are seeking Jesus in the Scripture as never before. Many grew up in an era when the Church, busy doing other things, was not putting much energy into teaching the Bible. Some Catholics even picked up a kind of fear of Bible reading—as if the danger of false interpretation was so great that it was better to have nothing to do with the Bible at all. (As if a father would give his children a gift so dangerous it could not be used!)

Today there is a new emphasis on Scripture among Catholics. Bible study groups, an expanded selection of Scripture in the liturgy and encouragement from Church leaders have led many Catholics to dust off the family Bible, looking for nourishment for the spiritual life.

Unfortunately, many new students of Scripture quickly experience frustration and confusion. This need not happen if they start with a solid introduction on how to approach the Bible.

Two basic principles should guide us each time we pick up the Bible: (1) The Bible is both the Word of God and the words of human beings. (2) The Bible is not a book—it is a library.

The Bible is divine *and* human

First, the Bible is at the same time both the Word of God and the words of human beings. We have the same problem understanding the Bible as we have understanding Jesus. We believe that he is at once both fully human and fully divine. It is a mystery we cannot totally comprehend.

Because he is human, Jesus sometimes displays *human* ignorance. In Mark's Gospel, for example, he tells us that he does not know the time of the Second Coming (13:32). We are shocked that the Incarnate Son of God could be ignorant of such an important matter. Yet our experience tells us that to be fully human, as we experi-

ence humanity, is to be ignorant of many things. So, though it remains a mystery, we believe the Gospel which tells us that Jesus could be ignorant.

The Bible, too, is at the same time divine and human. It is truly God's Word, and when we read it prayerfully we experience its power to bring us into contact with the Lord. Yet it is embarrassingly human. The human authors show a woeful ignorance of science, history and even theology, because God uses as authors human beings with all their limitations.

The author of Genesis knew nothing of what modern science has discovered about the solar system. To that writer, the earth was a flat disk, and the sky a solid dome, like a bowl turned upside down over a saucer. Above the bowl was a great ocean. The dome, or "firmament," had windows which the Lord could open at will to allow some of the water stored above to come down in the form of rain.

God did not free the inspired author from the scientific ignorance shared with the people of that time; God simply used those inaccurate ideas to get across his own message: that he had created everything that exists. So Genesis tells us that God created the firmament, and the Psalms tell us that he opens the windows when he chooses to send rain. The person of faith, as he or she reads, must sort out the human from the divine in the Bible.

Unfortunately, the sorting is not always quite as easy as in this example. Fortunately, each reader does not have to do the sorting alone, because we receive help from the Church: both from official statements and from the writings of the many women and men of faith who have made the study of the Bible their life's work. But it never ceases to be a mystery how a book can be God's Word and yet be so thoroughly human.

The Bible is a library

The second principle we need to remember in reading the Bible is that this is not really a book; it is a *library*. Like the books on the typical library shelf, the 73 books of the Bible have been written at various dates over a period of a thousand years, and in a variety of literary forms.

An intelligent library user will look at the copyright date of a book. A biology book written in 1920 will not tell us anything of the scientific advances made since that date. The Book of Genesis was written long before modern science or the theory of evolution, and cannot tell us anything on those subjects.

We notice great differences between ideas contained in one book of the Bible and another. Psalm 30 clearly denies that human beings can experience happiness after death; the later Books of Daniel and Maccabees do speak of life after death. The Book of Deuteronomy permits divorce; the prophet Malachi says that God detests it; Jesus calls remarriage after divorce adultery. Many other contradictions could be listed. This is because the Bible, like any library, gathers books written at various stages in the ongoing process of human development.

God's relationship with his people, like every human relationship, is a developing relationship. A man may fall in love with a woman in a split second, but between that moment and the celebration of their golden wedding anniversary there is a long process of growth in the relationship, with all the ups and downs and joys and pains of human growth. He will speak of her differently at each stage. The same is true of God. He reveals himself and his will gradually to his people, trying not to overwhelm them at any point with more truth than they can handle. He takes us where we are, and leads us toward fuller truth.

For instance, the ancient Israelites shared the idea of woman held by men of the Ancient Near East. She was the property of man, much as his sheep or cattle were, valuable mainly because of her ability to give pleasure to man and to bear him male children. Bit by bit through the Scripture, God revealed the human dignity of woman.

In the early books of the Old Testament a man is allowed to have as many wives as he can support. He can have them all at once, or he can divorce one when he grows tired of her and marry another. The only protection given the woman is that he must give her a bill of divorce, which frees her to remarry. But by the time the Books of Tobit or Malachi were written, late in the Old Testament period, an ideal of marital love and fidelity has emerged which is much closer to our own.

Still later, St. Paul proclaims a basic equality between men and women when he says that in Christ there is neither male nor female (see Galatians 3:28). We find all these views of women within a few pages of each other in our Bible, but we have to remember that they were written centuries apart, as may be the case with books that stand side by side on the library shelf.

What God tells his people to do changes very much from one part of the Bible to another, also. It is not that God changes his mind, but that his people are gradually growing to maturity, and what was suitable at one period of their growth is not suitable later. It is not so different from the relationship between a human father and son. The father may command his five-year-old son, with great emphasis and threats of dire punishment, that he must never under any conditions cross the street without holding the hand of an adult. But if that son at the age of 21 continued to feel bound by that command, we would know that something was very wrong.

In the early parts of the Old Testament, God is said to command his people to conquer Palestine from its settled inhabitants, and to kill every man, woman and child in the conquered cities. But later on, the Book of Jonah shows God actually loving the pagan enemies of Israel, and disapproving of Jonah's desire that they all be consumed by fire from heaven. Jesus, finally, comes to save all women and men, and teaches his people to love their enemies.

The fundamentalists who think that every command in the Bible is to be obeyed today run into endless contradictions. They do not understand that in the library of the Bible some parts of some books are simply dated. They are valuable because they trace the process of God's growing relationship with his people, but they should not be followed literally today.

Even the books of the New Testament have become outdated in some details. No one today observes the order of the Council of Jerusalem found in the Acts of the Apostles that Christians eat only kosher meat, or St. Paul's command that slaves must obey their masters. St. Paul's other orders, that women must have their heads covered and keep silence in church, are rapidly becoming dated now.

So, in this library of the Bible, it is helpful to know the date of publication of any particular book. That enables us to understand it in its context and avoid expecting final answers from the books that were written during the earlier phases of God's revelation.

The literary form matters

It is also very important to know the *literary form* of any book you choose from the library shelf. A modern library contains history textbooks, historical novels, scientific studies, science fiction, and works of philosophy, theology and fantasy. A biblical author who picked up any one of these books might misunderstand it totally because of the unfamiliar literary form. Similarly, the modern reader can totally misunderstand the biblical authors because many of the literary forms they use are no longer in use, and we do not know what to make of them.

Accustomed to reading scientific accounts of the origins of the world and of humankind, we pick up the Book of Genesis and imagine that we are reading the same kind of thing. In reality, the first 11 chapters of Genesis contain no scientific statements; the author lived at a period when the very concept of modern scientific investigation had not entered the human mind. Genesis is a theological work, and the literary form in which the theological insights are expressed is the ancient form sometimes called *myth,* which presents profound realities in the form of symbolic stories.

Beginning with Chapter 12 of Genesis we come to a different literary form. We might call it "family reminiscences." It is comparable to the stories and tidbits of memories that might be recounted by the older generation at a big family reunion. Are the stories that are handed down about the eccentricities of great-great-grandfather O'Leary exactly true, or have they improved a good deal with repeated telling? No one knows for sure, and it really does not matter. They are a delightful part of the family heritage. In the same way, Jews of every age remembered their first ancestors Abraham and Sarah, and these memories were eventually collected into Chapters 12 through 50 of Genesis.

Other parts of the Bible, such as the Books of Kings or Chronicles, deal more with what we call real history: kings and battles and other events of national or international importance.

Still other parts of the Bible are pure poetry. The Song of Songs is a collection of love songs, perhaps once used in the wedding festivities of the Israelites. The Book of Psalms is a collection of hymns, written by many authors at many different periods, later collected and placed under the patronage of King David, much as in our time the hymns in the *Pius X Hymnal* were written by many individuals, then collected into one book and placed under the patronage of Pope Pius X.

Finally, other parts of the Bible can be described as "didactic fiction." The story of the Good Samaritan does not tell of an actual incident; it is a parable teaching love of neighbor. The Books of Ruth, Esther, Tobit and Jonah are also didactic fiction. The reader who worries about how the whale swallowed Jonah without chewing him has really missed the point, and also the fun. Jonah is a cartoon, a delightful satire about the narrow-minded Jew who brings all his vehement prejudices against non-Jews to a mighty and hilarious battle with God, who loves Jew and non-Jew alike.

The Christian who panics when hearing that Jonah is a work of fantasy, fearing that the Gospels may also be works of fantasy, is not remembering that the Bible is a library. One does not dismiss the truth of every book in the library because the library contains some novels. For the beginner, it is important to have a modern translation, such as the *New American Bible,* which provides introductions to each book. These introductions clue the reader in as to what kind of literature he or she is reading.

Where to open your Bible

What is the best way to begin reading this library which is the Bible? One way *not* to do it is by starting at page one and plowing through to the end. That makes about as much sense as starting with the first book on the top shelf of the library and reading every book in order. The Bible was just not meant to be read that way, and most readers who try it lose their enthusiasm before they get through Leviticus. The fact of the matter is that the beginning student entering a new library needs to consult either the librarian or a bibliography to get any order into his or her reading.

One good place to begin is the Acts of the Apostles. This is the story of the early Church, and especially of the missionary work of St. Paul. It is not difficult to catch the author's excitement about the work of the Spirit in the newborn Christian community. Those who have lived through the past 20 years of Church history will have little difficulty in seeing the similarities between what those first Christians experienced and what the post-Vatican II Church has lived through.

After reading in Acts about the early Christians of Thessalonica and Corinth and Philippi, it becomes much more interesting to read the letters St. Paul wrote to those churches.

These letters will arouse your curiosity about the first books of the Bible, to which Paul often

refers, and you will enjoy reading Genesis, Exodus and Deuteronomy. By then you will be ready to reread the Gospels, noticing the new light that is cast on many passages by your Old Testament reading. Then you might want to turn to the Book of Psalms, which summarizes the history and spirituality of the Old Testament, and contains the prayers actually used by Jesus, Mary and all the first Christians. By this point, the Bible will have become a world familiar to you. You will have visited its high points and will be ready to explore whichever of the lesser paths may appeal to you.

You may want to make your journey of discovery through the Bible with no help but the introductions and footnotes in your Bible itself. Or you may feel more secure using a commentary such as the volumes of the *Old Testament Message* and *New Testament Message* published by Michael Glazier, Inc., or the *Collegeville Bible Commentary* published by Liturgical Press. If you are the kind of person who often asks questions about specific persons or things as you read, you might keep at hand John McKenzie's *Dictionary of the Bible,* for quick access to a great quantity of information.

There are many ways of reading the Bible, one better for one person, another for someone else. But the most important element of any Christian's approach to the Bible is that it be done prayerfully, with faith and humility. By faith we know that this is God's Word, with power to change our lives. By humility we know that, due to our human limitations, we will never understand it totally. If we approach the Bible prayerfully—keeping in mind that it is both the Word of God and the words of limited human beings, and that it is not a book but a library—we will discover the spiritual nourishment that God has placed there for us.

This article originally appeared as *Catholic Update* #124 (1984), published by St. Anthony Messenger Press, Cincinnati, Ohio.

3. THE DELIVERANCE AT THE SEA

The description of the Exodus in the Bible was compiled from two earlier accounts. Scholars have sorted out which parts of the biblical account come from each of the earlier accounts. Here are the two earlier accounts as they have been reconstructed by scholars.

THE YAHWIST-ELOHIST (JE) ACCOUNT

13:20-22 They moved on from Succoth and encamped at Etham, on the edge of the wilderness. And the Lord went before them by day in a pillar of cloud to lead them along the way, and by night in a pillar of fire to give them light, so they could travel by day and night; the pillar of cloud by day and the pillar of fire by night did not depart from in front of the people.

14:5-7 When it was reported to the King of Egypt that the people had fled, Pharaoh and his servants changed their minds about them. They said "What is this we have done that we have let Israel go from our service?" So he made ready his chariot and took his army with him — six hundred first-class chariots and all the other chariots of Egypt, with warriors on them all.

14:10a When the Pharaoh drew near, the people of Israel looked up and saw the Egyptians marching after them. And they were terrified...

14:11-14 And they complained to Moses: "Is it because there were no graves in Egypt that you have brought us away to die in the wilderness? Why did you do this to us? Why did you bring us out of Egypt? Leave us alone and let us serve the Egyptians. For it would have been better for us to serve the Egyptians than to die in the wilderness." And Moses said to the people, "Fear not, stand firm, and you will see the victory the Lord will win for you today; for the Egyptians you see now you will never see again. The Lord himself will fight for you; you only have to keep still."

THE PRIESTLY (P) ACCOUNT

14:1-4 Then the Lord said to Moses, "Tell the Israelites to turn back and to camp in front of Pi-ha-hiroth, between Migdol and the sea. You shall camp opposite Baal-zephon by the sea. Pharaoh will say, 'The Israelites are wandering about in the land, and the wilderness has shut them in.' And I will harden Pharaoh's heart, and he will pursue them and I shall receive glory through Pharaoh and all his army. The Egyptians will know that I am the Lord."

14:8-9 And the Lord hardened the heart of the Pharaoh, King of Egypt, so that he pursued the people of Israel while they were leaving triumphantly. The Egyptians pursued them, all Pharaoh's horses and chariots and his horsemen and his army, and overtook them encamped by the sea, at Pi-ha-hiroth, opposite Baal-zephon.

14:10b and the people cried out to the Lord.

14:15-18 The Lord said to Moses, "Why do you cry out to me? Tell the Israelites to go forward. Lift up your staff and stretch out your hand over the sea. Divide it so the Israelites can go through the sea on dry ground. I will harden the hearts of the Egyptians so that they will follow them,

THE YAHWIST-ELOHIST (JE) ACCOUNT

14:19–20, 21b   The angel of God who had led them now moved behind them. The pillar of cloud also moved from in front and stood behind them so that it came between the camp of the Egyptians and the camp of the Israelites. The cloud became dark, and the night passed without the two camps coming nearer. And the Lord drove the sea back by a strong east wind all night, and made the sea dry land.

14:24–25   In the watch before dawn, the Lord in the pillar of fire and cloud looked on the Egyptians and struck terror into them. He clogged their chariot wheel so they could hardly drive. And the Egyptians said, "Let us flee from Israel, for the Lord fights for them against the Egyptians."

14:27b   At dawn the sea flowed back while the Egyptians were fleeing head-on into it, and the Lord hurled them into its midst.

14:28b   Not a single one of them escaped.

14:30-31   Thus the Lord saved Israel that day from the hand of the Egyptians and Israel saw them dead on the seashore. When Israel saw the great work that the Lord had done against the Egyptians, they feared the Lord and believed in the Lord and in his servant Moses.

THE PRIESTLY (P) ACCOUNT

and I will receive glory through Pharaoh and all his army, his chariots and his horsemen. And the Egyptians will know that I am the Lord, when I have received glory over Pharaoh, his chariots, and his horsemen."

14:21a, 22–23   Then Moses stretched his hand over the sea and the waters were divided. And the Israelites went into the midst of the sea on dry ground, with the water like a wall to their right and their left. The Egyptians pursued them into the midst of the sea, all Pharaoh's horses, his chariots and charioteers.

14:26   Then the Lord said to Moses, "Stretch out your hand over the sea, that the waters may come back on the Egyptians, on their chariots and charioteers."

14:27a   So Moses stretched forth his hand over the sea

14:28a   And the waters returned and covered the chariots and the charioteers and all the army of Pharaoh which was pursuing them through the sea.

14:29   But the Israelites walked on dry ground through the sea, the waters like a wall to their left and to their right.

4. THE DESERT: A ROUNDABOUT WAY

By Fr. Robert Wild

The wilderness or desert is one of the major themes of the bible. "The wilderness was the decisive period in Israel's primeval history." If we consider the history of God's dealings with Israel as normative for our own personal relationship with Yahweh, then an understanding and a reliving of what happened to Israel in the desert is crucial to our own life with God. Have we ever given much serious thought to the idea that a desert experience may be part of revelation for each one of us, the revelation of an experience and a situation in the life of God's people which each one of us somehow must share? Although there are four different words used to describe wilderness or desert in the bible, the one most frequently used refers to the sojourn of Israel after its exodus from Egypt.

God's people were eager, we presume, to get out of Egypt, with all its back-breaking work and everything that accompanies the condition of slavery. But not too long after their departure, the difficulties of Egypt looked very good compared to the situation they now found themselves in. We too are so at home and comfortable with our sicknesses of all kinds that we'd rather stay with them than start on the road to health. At least we can manage in our state of illness. We know who we are and even though we are sick we are surviving. We feel some of our diseases slipping away from us as we enter the desert, and the prospect of health frightens us. The world of total purification might be more terrifying than Egypt. "The wilderness is the place that threatens the very existence of Yahweh's chosen people."

Why is the desert threatening? It is threatening because it is the place which lacks all the supports which we believe are necessary for our existence. Ordinary dialogue with many people is absent. Other people are one of our main supports for reassuring us that we are not alone in the universe. We give lip service to the fact that there is Another present in our lives, the Person of all persons. But in the desert we are actually challenged to put all our trust in this Other. We must now put our lives where our pious thoughts gave us the illusion of being "at home" with God. We must learn to say from experience, "Lord, You are people and presence and company enough for me." It is in the desert where that sentence no longer is beautiful poetry but a matter of life and death.

The desert is threatening because of the silence and the absence of activity normally associated with "living." We matter-of-factly equate noise and activity with living. When something is happening, or better, when we are making something happen, we are reassured that we are not nothing. In the desert we are challenged to experience that simply to be is the greatest and most fundamental activity of which we are capable. We are challenged to experience whether we can live meaningfully at this most basic level. We are challenged to say (again, not as mere pious phrases, but as utter reality), "Lord, You are my life." Ordinarily we say this and then get on with other things just in case the Lord is not sufficient.

If we are willing to experience the loss of these superficial aspects of existence for a while, then God can manifest his power. "The wilderness . . . is also the stage which brightly illumines God's power and readiness to dispel the threat." God actually upholds us all the time by his power. But there are dimensions of realizing this power which we can foster by concretely relinquishing the superficial supports of Egypt. Will we allow the conscious realization of his power to enter us by and through a desert experience? Yahweh knows that the desert can be this place of discovery of his power and his presence, and that is why he leads us into it.

Our radical dependence on God is not an occasional event, occurring perhaps once a week. It is constant. This is a hard lesson to learn and to live out. The teaching of this lesson was part of Yahweh's desert discipline: "Yahweh helps his people in the wilderness from day to day. Israel is not permitted to live in security lest she forget that she is utterly dependent on her God." The time in the desert is a time of experiencing constant dependence. Our temptation is to call on God from time to time when life gets shaky; for the rest we are under the illusion of coasting on our own. The temptation of the people in the desert was to continue this pseudo-existence by demanding large amounts of bread so that they would not be wondering all night whether God would feed them on the morrow.

But God does not give over-flowing storehouses of superficial food in the desert. He fed his people only one day at a time. Outside the desert, where the illusion of supporting ourselves is normal, planning and filling granaries is part of life. We rest secure in our storehouses. We turn to God occasionally to thank him for the abundance and maybe panic a bit when they start to diminish. In the desert the storehouses are always empty. It is a time for learning total dependence, minute by minute.

The disorientation and confusion of the desert is preparatory to deeper encounters. "(Several) decisive events take place in the wilderness which are once and for all decisive and normative for the religious life of Israel. The first of these crucial events is the revelation of God's name."

Each person is a little universe of his own, and each person experiences reality in a slightly different way than the next person. This is also true of our experience and our relationship with God. Although we all give him the same name—God—he is actually special to each one of us and in some way we have our own special name for him—what he is or means *for us*. In the desert, when the supports of our personal world are removed, a new name for God emerges and is revealed to us. Just as in the history of Israel God's name actually changed as they experienced him in different cultures and situations, so in our personal lives, God's name, in a way, is constantly changing, or ought to. Depending on the kinds of Egypts we are trying to leave behind, God will reveal himself to us in the desert as "He-who-gives-me-courage," or as "He-who-upholds-me-in-darkness," or as "He-who-is-personal-center-of-everything." In the desert God will reveal his name to us, just as he revealed it to Moses (Ex 3:6).

By this revelation of his name, God makes the desert the place where personal relationship begins. Introduction, introducing ourselves, is the first step to conversation. "It becomes possible to say that Israel's religious life as a partner of Yahweh begins in the wilderness. The desert is the place of God's initial and fundamental revelation to his people." The desert is, therefore, a covenant-making place and a law-giving place. It's a strange paradox to say that although Israel left Egypt as a people they were not yet a people, a unity, with a common bond and a common God. In the desert God put order into their chaos. Out of a multitude of disunited tribes he formed a people. Their unity came about by all of them facing together the mountain of God and pledging their loyalty and their lives.

It is similar with us. We enter the desert presumably as a whole person and yet we quickly discover our fragmentation. We too are like a loose federation of warring tribes. Through the nakedness of a desert experience God wishes to unify us, to experience the basic laws of our life with him, to allow us to experience these laws as sources of life. Through a kind of unification, a vague and general "God" becomes "my God," and the universal "Word to mankind" becomes "God's Word to me." The wilderness was the "womb of the religion of the Old Testament." Could it be that such must be the case for each one of us, a desert experience where personal covenant becomes a reality which unifies our fragmentation?

Total dependence is a hard lesson to learn. Because the desert is without any "visible means of support," it is the place where our lack of trust and faith stand out most glaringly. "The desert is also the scene of Israel's sin which comes to light at once." God, we quickly discover, is not enough for us. We rejoiced for a little while as he fed us, as he revealed his new name, as he disclosed to us the basic laws of life. But we forget easily. Soon we begin to murmur and hanker after the life of Egypt. We can stand just so much reality. The great temptation periodically in the desert is to *get out.*

"Israel makes an attempt to shorten the time of waiting, seeking to escape the desert before God allows them to do so." This is our temptation too, to "shorten the time," to make our time-table God's time-table, and to arrange our stay in the desert just long enough to make it interesting without endangering our normal supports. Until the Lord comes in all his fullness, we need some idol to hold onto. Outside the desert substitutes for God remain more firm. In the desert the only image the Lord will allow us is his *changing name,* as we have the courage to allow his presence more and more to enter our lives. But such a shifting relationship is too elusive for us. We need some static idols, some visible images to rest in a while before we continue on our journey. "The revelation of the name of God is forgotten in exchange for a visible image."

Thomas Merton once wrote that many people leave Egypt but very few enter the Promised Land. We sense the need to leave Egypt, but after we get in the desert we are not so sure. The delights of the desert can only be revealed by crossing it and by trusting in the Lord.

There is a beautiful passage in Exodus on how delicately the Lord deals with us in this journey. "When Pharaoh had let the people go, God did not let them take the road to the land of the Philistines, although that was the nearest way. God thought that the prospect of fighting would make the people lose heart and turn back to Egypt. Instead, God led the people by the roundabout way of the wilderness to the Sea of Reeds"

(13:17–18). In Yahweh's travel plans for us, the desert often seems like a waste of time and truly a roundabout way of getting to the heart of the matter. We would like to strike straight ahead and cut the Philistines down, get to the Promised Land and be done with it. Why all this desert stuff? In the Lord's mind, it seems that before we can fight the philistines in our lives and in our society, we must learn the art of life's warfare at its deepest level. And what is the plan of battle in the wilderness? Paradox of paradoxes, it is to keep still and let Yahweh fight for us: "Moses answered the people: 'Have no fear! Stand firm, and you will see what Yahweh will do to save you today: the Egyptians you see today you will never see again. *Yahweh will do the fighting for you: you have only to keep still'*" (Ex. 14:13-14).

In the desert we learn how to live in the rhythm of the well-springs of Life if we can allow all our superficial supports to fall by the wayside as we journey. In the desert that most nagging of all questions of man—"Is Yahweh with us or not" (Ex. 17:7)—will be experienced and answered with a depth and clarity we never dreamed possible: "Now I know that Yahweh is greater than all the gods" (Ex. 18:12).

Fr. Wild, who has been Trappist, Carthusian, and parish priest, resides in Combermere where he lives in solitude several days a week, spending the rest of his time with the Madonna House Community.

5. WHY IS THE BIBLE LIKE A CAMEL?

By Sr. Macrina Scott, O.S.F.

The Bible is God's word, but God speaks that word through a variety of human beings, each with his own style and point of view. God inspired Isaiah, Jeremiah, Mark, John, and Paul, but each of these men communicated God's word through his own particular culture, time, and personality. Those who have read the Bible carefully have always noticed this variety of human authorship.

Modern biblical scholars have come to a clearer understanding of the way in which God speaks through the human authors of the Bible — an understanding which teaches us about God's ways of dealing with His people. We sometimes imagine that God speaks only through a few very special individuals, that most of us can only listen and repeat what we hear, that we have nothing to contribute to His message. But scholars have discovered that some books of the Bible, including the first four — Genesis, Exodus, Leviticus, and Numbers — were not written by one person, but are more like committee reports composed of ideas given by God to several different people. We do not know the real names of the principal three authors whose ideas have been combined in these books, but scholars call them P (the priest), J (the Yahwist), and E (the Elohist).

Committee reports are not usually the easiest things to read; they are not likely to flow as smoothly as something written by a single individual. And those who have taken part in writing them know the long and painful process of discussion from which the report comes. Neither those who read a committee report nor those who write it are often aware that the Spirit may speak through such a group process as truly as the Spirit may speak through an inspired individual.

Those who have struggled in putting together committee reports like to tell the story of the acute observer who was watching a camel ambling around in its ungainly way, as if all the parts didn't fit together properly in its huge body. The observer, who had participated in putting together many a committee report, commented, "It looks like a horse that was created by a committee."

Those who have studied the first four books of the Old Testament have had a similar impression. By ordinary literary standards, the parts don't fit properly together. There are repetitions and contradictions and sudden shifts of style. On the same page different names are used for God, or for the persons or places. The general impression is of an unwieldy mass of parts that don't quite fit together. Biblical scholars, acute observers that they are, attribute this problem to committee writing.

It was a most unusual kind of committee, for its members lived some hundreds of years apart. Thus the committee chairman, whom they call P (the priest), has had more than a fair share of influence on the committee report. The other committee members were dead, and unable to fight for their fair share at the time when he combined the works they had left behind with his own work.

Both they and we have a lot for which we should be grateful to P. He was a priest who served God's people at a time of crisis when it seemed likely that faith in the true God would be lost altogether. Since Solomon's time, the people of Judah had centered their religion and their government at Jerusalem, in the Temple of Yahweh and the palace of the kings descended from David. But only a few years before the priest's time, in 587 B.C., the whole of Jerusalem had been leveled to the ground by the terrible Babylonian war machine, and the people themselves had been carried off as exiles to Babylon. There they were surrounded by stories and celebrations of the Babylonian gods. It would have been natural for them to shift allegiance to the new gods in whose land they lived, gods who seemingly had proved themselves more powerful than Yahweh. The marvel is that they did not. Men like the priest made a tremendous effort to collect the various religious writings they had been able to rescue from the conflagration of Jerusalem, edit and combine them into a great account of their sacred history that could inspire them to faithfulness even in the dark times of the Exile.

One of the precious manuscripts which P had to work with contained reports of two committee members which had already been combined. Biblical scholars called one J, for Yahweh, because he generally calls God Yahweh. (These scholars were mainly German, and Yahweh begins with J in German.) The other they called E because in the first part of his story he always calls God Elohim, saying that the name Yahweh was only revealed to Moses at the burning bush.

J had lived in the southern part of the country; E in the north. Both had gathered the stories circulated orally in their parts of the country about the sacred history of God's people, and had arranged them into a great written saga, stressing the moral message needed by their contemporaries.

J composed his saga about 950 B.C., at the end of the one period of worldly glory the chosen people ever knew, the years when all twelve tribes were united under King David, and his son Solomon. At last they felt they were a kingdom, on a par with neighboring kingdoms. They were no longer twelve tribes, each struggling for survival among the hostile Canaanites. For the first time, there was a king able to sponsor great architecture and literary work, and eager to do so, as kings of great kingdoms did.

Solomon was fortunate to have a genius of the quality of J at hand, someone eager to gather the traditions that had been handed down orally for so long into a great literary and theological work which would show God's special love for His people, and the way in which God's plan had been at work from the creation of the world, preparing for the glorious Davidic dynasty. The recurring

theme was promise-fulfillment: all God's promises in the old era were finally fulfilled in the new era which had dawned with King David. (For a list of the passages which make up the Yahwist's story, see "The Yahwist Passages from the Pentateuch," # 10 below in the SUPPLEMENTARY READINGS.)

But J was not merely a propagandist for his patron, King Solomon. He had a great insight into and love for human nature, so his work is full of fascinating characters and stories. Each hero — Noah, Abraham, Jacob, Joseph, Moses — comes across as a unique personality with strengths and weaknesses. The great and holy patriarch Abraham lies unabashedly, presenting his wife Sarah as his sister in order to save his own skin. In his version of the story, E, the Elohist, tries to gloss over the facts by explaining that she was in fact Abraham's half sister, but J makes no excuses. Readers sometimes complain that J's characters are not edifying, but never that they are dull.

J shows the depth of his psychological insights, particularly in his treatment of temptation and sin in the story of the fall in the Garden of Eden. Perhaps he is thinking of events in his own time, e.g., Bathsheba's seduction of David, and all the evil it brought the nation, when he describes Eve and the forbidden fruit so vividly.

Even God seems delightfully human in J's stories. God does not create the world with one all-powerful statement, as in the P creation account. He plants a garden with loving care for people to live in, and then He kneels down and takes some of its earth and carefully shapes Adam with His own fingers, as a sculptor shapes a statue. Into the figure He has shaped, He breathes His own breath. Later, He carefully seals the door of the ark shut from the outside to protect Noah and all creatures with him, but He can also be so disappointed and angry at sin that He regrets ever having created human beings.

J was a literary artist who portrayed human experience in a way that speaks to every generation. But he was also a man with a very specific purpose for his own times. Sudden power and affluence were heady wine for a people whose memories were all of slavery, nomadic wandering in the desert, and generations of grueling guerrilla warfare by which they penetrated foot by foot into the land promised to them. It was a new and wonderful era, and Israelites naturally looked to the great nations to see how to adapt to the situation. They noticed the religious myths and the gods these nations claimed as their protectors. These gods were closely connected with the king himself, and gave him almost unlimited power. Kingship was a new phenomenon in Israel. How natural it would have been to borrow some of the neighboring myths to place the Davidic king on the same divine level as the surrounding kings.

The Yahwist devoted his whole energy to composing a great statement against this natural trend. Israel had no need of gods or god-kings like those of its neighbors. The old sacred stories that had been passed down by word of mouth in every tribe for generations could reveal new meaning in the new situation, if only they were gathered and shaped into one great literary work with this purpose in mind. These stories showed Israel that Yahweh was far from outdated: in fact, it was He who promised and had been preparing since the creation for this great time. From these stories Israel could learn a concept of kingship different from that of her pagan neighbors.

The king in Israel was to be human, not divine. He was to be subject to God, who would speak to him through the prophets. If he disobeyed, trouble would fall on him and his kingdom. In response to the temptations of his time, J produced a concept that would continue as an ideal through all of Hebrew and Christian history: the authority of a political leader is not absolute, but is subject to God and to God's law.

J gathered and retold the old stories in a way that not only delighted the people of his time, but showed them that the old faith had a message for new times.

Soon after the death of Solomon, the glorious kingdom fell apart. The saga of J continued to be read and recited at religious festivals in the southern kingdom of Judah, where the descendants of David still ruled over a small nation. The larger northern kingdom continued to use its version of the old stories, one which did not give such prominence to the southern tribes or to David, and attached more importance to Jacob and to Moses. E gathered these traditions — in about 850 B. C. — as J had gathered those in the South. He told many of the same stories, but his approach lacked the warm human interest of J. His heroes are a trifle stiff, a bit less than human.

E's God is far above the human scene, and enters it only indirectly by way of angels and dreams, never simply walking among His creatures as J's God did. E wrote at a time when the great temptation surrounding Israel was that of the Canaanite cult of Baal. The conflict between Elijah and priests of Baal shows the intensity of the struggle. E's message was that the God of Israel was the God to be worshipped: He tolerated no compromise. E tells the story of Abraham sacrificing his only son Isaac to illustrate the total dedication expected by God.

Unfortunately, we do not know very much about E. The northern kingdom was conquered by the Assyrians in 721 B.C., the ten tribes were scattered, never to come together again as a people. A few refugees escaped to the southern kingdom. One of them brought a copy of E to Jerusalem.

In Jerusalem, E was read with interest, but of course it could in no way replace the well-loved J. However, it did add some stories, some fresh details for the old stories, and a greater sense of the transcendence of God and the danger of unfaithfulness to Him. So an enthusiastic southern scholar combined the two, keeping J as the main basis, but adding what appealed to him from E, fitting the two together as well as his editorial abilities permitted, but without concern for clarity and consistency a modern editor would have. This edition, called JE, is what the priest had to work with.

E was like a committee member from another part of the country, with different information and a different theology to contribute, whose personality was not forceful enough to get a full hearing for what he had to say. Much of E has been lost, but the committee report was enriched by the bits that were preserved.

Both J and E were lay theologians, interested mainly in the ways in which God worked in the history of His people. But P had another source, D, the Deuteronomist, who was also of the priestly class and so shared his interest in liturgical matters and in the laws which were administered by the priests, since no class of professional lawyers yet existed. D, like E, was from the ill-fated northern kingdom.

D was interested in the law, but not in any cold, legalistic way. The great reality for him was God's love for His people, and the law was a gift which led the people to the fullness of life and gave them a way of responding to God's love. His style is more that of a sermon — at times an impassioned exhortation — than that of a modern law book. It may well be that D actually wrote down these traditional laws, which had evolved out of centuries of experience, only after the defeat of the northern kingdom, when they were no longer the official law of the land. He may have written them more as an idealized law, a dream for the restoration of the northern kingdom, which was never to take place. In any case, he brought a copy of his dream to the Temple in Jerusalem. There, like so many library books, it rested for most of a century without anyone being aware of its existence. But in 622 B.C. it was discovered by some workmen making repairs in the Temple.

D's hour had come. King Josiah was intent on religious and political reform, and the laws of D, and his exhortations for faithfulness, were just what Josiah needed to give authority and direction to his reform.

Unfortunately, the reform, which P may have remembered from his own childhood, had been short-lived. But the book that had done so much to shape it was sacred to him, and he did not chop it up and combine its parts into his committee report. It had a distinctive flavor that deserved to

be preserved separately. After P had completed his report, D would be added to it as a separate book. Deuteronomy, a kind of minority report appended to the main one, because it could not be assimilated.

P thought the most important thing he had to work with was the accumulated traditions of the Jerusalem priesthood which he had been taught from childhood, of which he had some written records, and about which he could consult his fellow priests in exile. This was his own heritage. His task was to organize it into a written form which could serve the exiles as a kind of program for the restoration that was their dream. When Yahweh finally took pity on his people and freed them from exile, they would return to Jerusalem carrying P's book containing every detail of God's law about the Temple they must rebuild, the services they must conduct there, and the whole life of the people consecrated to God's service.

P was not as good a storyteller as J or E, but he would have made a good canon lawyer or expert on liturgical rules. The Book of Leviticus, which contains most of the laws, might make a good legal reference work if properly indexed, but it makes dull reading.

Everything about P is well organized. He has preserved interminable genealogies to show every possible relationship. His sources contain stories, especially about the early period, but his interest in history is more in the overall organization of the various periods than in the flesh-and-blood people and their experiences. But what he lacks in the detailed human interest kind of historical writing, he makes up for in the overall vision he gives of Israel as a worshipping community, a people gathered around the Tent of Meeting which represented God's presence in their midst, a people whose entire life was to be dominated by the great command, "You must be holy, because I the Lord your God am holy." The complicated rules are not so lifeless as they seem, because they are only the practical ways of fulfilling P's ardent desire for holiness for God's people.

Part of P's wisdom was his recognition of the value of J's very different skills. So he incorporates much of J's great narrative into his own framework, using it to give life and color to his work. He is a committee chairman who does insist on having the last and strongest word, who wraps things up in the framework of his own thought, but also one who knows how to utilize the contributions of others that might otherwise have been lost.

It is relatively easy to imagine the Holy Spirit inspiring a man such as Jeremiah or Moses in such a way that what he speaks is truly God's word to us. But when we know the background of a committee report, or any document—such as those of Vatican II—which incorporates the ideas of many people and has been fashioned and refashioned through much heated debate, we do not so easily imagine the Spirit speaking through such complex processes of human interaction. But modern scholarship is showing us that that is precisely the way in which the Holy Spirit inspired the first four books of the Bible. It is a message of encouragement for weary committee members!

God's first disclosure in the drama of faith is his intrusion against an oppressive regime on behalf of those who are unable to liberate themselves. And the motif dominates that entire event and, indeed, all Israel's history. His way of letting himself be known is fundamental to biblical faith: "Let my people go." . . . The God of biblical faith is he who intrudes for freedom against every form of oppression, no matter how well ordered, seemingly legitimate or scientific it purports to be. . . . This is a massive affirmation desperately needed in our time. It affirms that human persons are willed by God to be free, not enslaved, oppressed or manipulated. It affirms that no regime or establishment from Pharaoh on out has any final claim over human life.

— Walter Brueggemann

6. THE SOURCES OF THE PENTATEUCH

Some Characteristics of The Yahwist (J)

The Yahwist, a southern writer, is a marvelous storyteller. His stories are very vivid, always concrete and full of imagery. God is often represented with human characteristics (anthropomorphism): in the creation story God is in turn a gardener, a potter, a surgeon, a tailor. That is the Yahwist's way of telling us about God and humanity; he proves to be a profound theologian.

God is a very human God who walks with Abraham as with a friend; has a meal with Abraham and bargains with him. People live on familiar terms with and meet God in everyday life.

However, this God is also a master who commands or forbids, who calls. "Go, leave," God says to Abraham and Moses. God has a plan for history. God's blessing will bring happiness to his people and through them will extend to all people. (It is remarkable to find such universalism at this period.) Humanity must respond to this divine call and obey God.

Humanity's sin is to want to take God's place. This sin draws down a curse: Cain, the flood, the tower of Babel. This is a God who is always ready to forgive, particularly when people like Abraham or Moses intercede with him, and always ready to renew his blessing.

The Yahwist exhibits fine character development and is especially interested in the tribe of Judah. Etymologies are often found in his stories.

The Yahwist uses the name Yahweh for God from the very beginning of Genesis, unlike the E and P writers who only begin to use this name after it is revealed to Moses in Exodus.

Some Characteristics of The Elohist (E)

These characteristics will be clearer if you compare the Elohist with the Yahwist.

He tends to be less vivid, less concrete.

God is utterly different from humanity. The Elohist usually avoids anthropomorphisms, or ways of talking about God as though God were human. This inaccessible God is revealed through dreams or angels. When God speaks in person, it is done through theophanies, or spectacular manifestations. One cannot make any image of the deity.

The Elohist is very interested in moral questions, and has a developing sense of sin. For example, he explains that Abraham never lied (compare Gn 12:10f (J) with Gn 20 (E). The law given Moses is less concerned with how to celebrate the cult than with morality, duty toward God and one's neighbor.

Real worship consists in obeying God and observing the covenant, rejecting all covenants with false gods.

The reflections of the Elohist, a Northern writer, are rooted in the prophetic tradition and the reflections of wise people.

Some Characteristics of The Priestly Writer (P)

The style of this southern tradition is dry. The Priestly writer is not a storyteller. He loves figures and lists. He often repeats the same thing twice: God says ... God does. See, for example, his version of the crossing of the Red Sea, the creation, the building of the Ark and Tabernacle. The vocabulary is often technical and has to do with the cult.

Genealogies appear often. They give the people roots in history and connect up this history with that of the creation.

Worship has pride of place. Moses organizes it; Aaron and his descendants are made responsible for continuing it through pilgrimages, festivals, and worship in the temple, which is the holy place in which God makes himself present. The priesthood is an essential institution which assures the existence of the people. Ritual is very important. Laws are usually put in a narrative context, so they are attached to historical events which give them significance. See, for example, the law of fertility (Gn 9:1) in the story of the flood, or the law of the Passover, attached to the tenth plague.

The Priestly writer experiences God as transcendent and holy and sees Israel as called to be holy because God is holy.

Some Characteristics of The Deuteronomist (D)

At a formal level:

– the style is very emotional. The author is not content to teach; he wants to convince people that they should obey.
– numerous repeated phrases, for example: the Lord your God ... Hear, O Israel, remember ... Keep the commandments, laws, and customs ...
– a constant mixture of the second person singular and the second person plural. In the book as it is now it becomes the affirmation that the people is a single body, but that each believer among this people keeps his/her own personality.

Some key ideas:

– The Lord is the sole God of Israel.
– God has chosen a people for himself. In response to this election, the people must love God.
– God has given the people a land, but on condition that they remain faithful, remember his covenant with them, today.
– It is above all in the liturgy that the people, an assembly called by God at Horeb, remembers and understands the word of God.

The Deuteronomist tradition originated in the North.

7. UNIT 1: MID-UNIT SELF-QUIZ

MATCHING: In the blanks before each statement, place the letter of the answer which is BEST described by the statement.

I. PERSONS

____	1.	led the women in song after the crossing of the sea	a. Aaron
____	2.	priest, brother of Moses	b. Amalekites
____	3.	wife of Moses	c. Habiru
____	4.	had an experience with God in the burning bush	d. Jethro
____	5.	group of slaves and oppressed people who escaped from Egypt	e. Joshua
____	6.	assistant of Moses, leader of the Israelite army	f. Levi
____	7.	father-in-law of Moses; priest of Midian	g. Miriam
____	8.	thought to be the Pharaoh at the time of the Exodus	h. Moses
____	9.	the tribe to which Aaron and Moses belonged	i. Rameses II
____	10.	the first group which the Israelites fought after their escape from Egypt	j. Zipporah

II. PLACES

____	11.	mountain of the burning bush and of the covenant	a. Goshen
____	12.	where Moses turned bitter water sweet	b. Horeb/Sinai
____	13.	crossed by the Israelites in their escape from Egypt	c. Marah
____	14.	source of Egypt's agricultural fertility	d. Midian
____	15.	city from which the Israelites left Egypt	e. Nile
____	16.	place where Moses fled into exile	f. Raamses
____	17.	area of Egypt where the Israelites had settled	g. Reed Sea

III. MULTIPLE CHOICE

____ 18.   The Pentateuch is also known as
   a. The Five Books of Moses   c. The Law
   b. The Torah   d. All of the above

According to many scripture scholars, there are four literary traditions or sources for the material in the Pentateuch. Name and correctly spell these four.

19. _____   21. _____

20. _____   22. _____

23. The Jewish feast which celebrates the Exodus is called _____.

24. The Israelites were fed with _____ and _____ in the desert.

ANSWERS TO MID-UNIT SELF-QUIZ

1.	g	10.	b	19.	Yahwist	
2.	a	11.	b	20.	Elohist	
3.	j	12.	c	21.	Deuteronomist	
4.	h	13.	g	22.	Priestly	
5.	c	14.	e	23.	Passover	
6.	e	15.	f	24.	Manna, Quail	
7.	d	16.	d			
8.	i	17.	a			
9.	f	18.	d			

ANSWERS: SELF-QUIZ ON THE DEUTERONOMIC HISTORY

1.	a	10.	r	17.	w
2.	t	11.	s	18.	j
3.	m	12.	f	19.	h
4.	n	13.	u	20.	p
5.	l	14.	d	21.	o
6.	g	15.	i	22.	c
7.	b	16.	e	23.	q
8.	v				
9.	k				

8. THE GENESIS OF LIBERATION: MOSES BOUND AND UNBOUND

by Lydia Champagne, C.S.J.

It is always a frightening thing to realize that the job you are called upon to do is a bigger one than you can handle and, in the midst of the fear, to know that it is completely possible for you to fall flat on your face and to fail others in the process. The experience of weakness and fear, of emptiness and poverty should establish immediate bonds between us and every other human being. But when the experience is deep, it shakes our foundations in such a way that we feel sure no one else has ever felt this way. As painful as this sort of experience may be, it is, I think, precisely the kind of thing that can propel us into liberation—our own, and consequently, that of many others. This was, it seems, the kind of experience Moses had which launched him onto the center stage of the whole history of salvation. It is in his story that we can read the genesis of liberation.

Moses Bound

In many ways his experience was similar to ours. In a world where hard labor and starvation were frightening realities for his Hebrew relatives, he was marked for privilege. He had the best of both worlds. Being reared a Hebrew by his own mother—at the expense of Pharaoh's daughter—gave him religious solidarity with his suffering kin along with a material security they could not have. He could know the facts about oppression from the inside without having to experience the hardship himself. When he took his place in Pharaoh's court, he was immune to all the laws which increased the weight of bondage for his fellow Hebrews. But his bond with his kin was strong enough to bring him into the political arena prematurely. As Exodus puts it: "Moses, a man by now, set out at this time to visit his countrymen, and he saw an Egyptian strike a Hebrew, one of

his countrymen. Looking around he could see no one in sight, so he killed the Egyptian and hid him in the sand" (Ex 2:11–12).

In one swift act of violence, the young Moses took a man's right to life into his own hands. His attempt to put an end to oppression was itself an act of oppression. Instead of making him the champion of his people, it made them suspect that they themselves were not safe in his presence.

The passage continues:

> On the following day he came back, and there were two Hebrews fighting. He said to the man who was in the wrong, "What do you mean by hitting your fellow countryman?" "And who appointed you," the man retorted, "to be prince over us, and judge? Do you intend to kill me as you killed the Egyptian?" (Ex 2:13–14)

The self-appointed liberator of his people discovered early in his career that the cure for violence is not greater violence, that the remedy for domination by an outsider is not domination by an insider. He had yet to learn that the liberation of others must begin in his own unliberated heart.

The remark of the Hebrew frightened him. Exodus continues: "'Clearly that business has come to light,' he thought. When Pharaoh heard of the matter he would have killed Moses, but Moses fled from Pharaoh and made for the land of Midian" (Ex 2:14-15). The swift vengeance of Moses did nothing to change the balance of power in Egypt. But it did precipitate a change in the future of Moses and of everyone else whose religious stance is somehow related to him.

Moses: The Fugitive

Moses entered the desert a fugitive rather than a contemplative. In his soul he was Hebrew, not

Egyptian. His heart was on the side of the underdog. He took his outrage with him to the land of Midian and vented it soon again on behalf of the oppressed, this time the women at the Midianite well. According to Exodus, male chauvinism was apparently rampant in the Midian desert. It says: "Now the priest of Midian had seven daughters. They came to draw water and fill the troughs to water their father's sheep. Shepherds came and drove them away, but Moses came to their defense and watered their sheep for them" (Ex 2:16-18). After this incident, at a safe distance from the inner city where the oppression of his people continued to increase, he quietly pastured his flocks. His frustration and alienation deepened, as indicated by the name he gave his first-born son. He called him Gershom, which means "I am a stranger in a foreign land."

As inviting as it is, no one who experiences solidarity with those who are suffering can settle permanently for the insulation of a Midian. But to leave our Midians when we alone decide that it is time can mean to leave them when we are as empty as when we came, with nothing to give those to whom we return. Moses maintained the delicate balance. His timing was right. The moment came when he saw the connection between his violent activism and his desert paralysis; between the desert outside him and the one inside; between his powerlessness and the strength of Yahweh. This was the moment when a bush in the desert blazed with a fire that did not destroy it but rather enhanced its beauty, and Moses knew that he stood on holy ground.

In his burning bush experience, he was purified by fire, as Isaiah would be later (Is 6:6–7), and the fire was the searing experience of the loving presence of God. But there was a Jeremiah in him, too, as he countered Yahweh's demands five times and five times had to give in: "'I will send you to Pharaoh to lead my people, the Israelites, out of Egypt,' Yahweh said. But Moses said to God, 'Who am I that I should go to Pharaoh and lead the Israelites out of Egypt?'" (Ex 3:10-11). It was a nec-

essary question because it articulated the awareness of his own powerlessness and evoked the strengthening assurance, "I will be with you." It also evoked the sign by which the mission of Moses would eventually be authenticated: "'The sign that I will give you,' Yahweh says, 'is this: When you bring my people out of Egypt, you will worship God on this very mountain'" (Ex 3:12).

The genuine contemplative experience does not isolate or insulate. It liberates people from their own narrow boundaries and sends them to liberate others, not just from physical oppression but from whatever keeps them from the total worship of God. We have abundant evidence that social reform does not automatically free human beings to do what they were created for and that the oppressed, once given their social and political freedom, often become oppressors. When Jesus himself rejected the temptation to turn stones into bread, he was rejecting a barren messiahship. He was able to feed the hungry, and did, but he refused to settle for bread alone or to allow his disciples to do so.

Moses would understand later the full significance of the promised sign that liberation would culminate in worship, but even as the bush burned, he feared that, without very persuasive credentials, he would never be able to mobilize the mob of slaves or force Pharaoh to bow to nonviolent resistance. "When I go to the Israelites and say to them, 'The God of your fathers has sent me to you,' if they ask me, 'What is his name?' what am I to tell them?" (Ex 3:13).

Scholars still debate the point of whether God's answer is a name or not, but apparently Moses had no problem with it. "I am who am" was for him a validation of the experience he was having. It meant this God is real, he is here, he will be with me, and that will make all the difference. One way of translating the Hebrew is "I will be there as who I am." This is an assurance of presence and transcendence. It is an assurance that the person who addresses him has the power to do the impossible and that he chooses to put it at the disposal of Moses. This Hebrew Prometheus does not have to steal his fire from the gods. Yahweh strikes the spark in Moses' heart and sends him to enkindle the flame in the heart of his people. The burning bush, the pillar of fire, the lightning of Sinai, the tongues of fire at Pentecost—all are images of the same burning presence which does not consume what it touches.

The transformation of Moses at this moment is dramatic. He still has his fears about returning to Egypt and speaking to Pharaoh, but having encountered the living God, he has a compelling mission. He is being sent into the heart of the political struggle to challenge the power of Pharaoh himself with no weapons except the power of God. In challenging the system, he is to spend no time on the periphery. He goes straight to the man at the center. Inexperienced apostles have shared the fear of Moses about the inadequacy of their words. But Yahweh gave the same assurance that was later reiterated by Jesus: "Do not worry about what you will say. You will be given power from on high."

Freedom Tested

By reason of this power, Moses becomes a new man. Yahweh sends the fearful fugitive to begin his new mission. His contemplative experience forces him to leave his desert and become a conscientious objector, a political activist, a social reformer, a community organizer, and the first of a long line of prophets.

The encounter of Moses with the living God gives him the courage he needs to return to Egypt and to begin the work he has been sent to do. But it does not change anyone else enough to make his job easy.

Yahweh had warned that Pharaoh would be obstinate, but who would have expected the Hebrews to resist their own deliverance? Moses has to learn for himself that for some mysterious reason, every slave loves his chains. When his first contact with Pharaoh brings retaliation on the brickmakers, they invoke the wrath of God on the well-intentioned Moses. There are no cheers from the mob as he and Aaron continue their collective bargaining in favor of the slaves. Even when they are finally on the march toward freedom, the mob complains about the itinerary! When they see Pharaoh's army in hot pursuit, their opposition to their own liberation becomes increasingly eloquent: "'Were there no burial places in Egypt,' they ask, 'that you had to bring us out here to die in the desert? Far better for us to be slaves of the Egyptians than to die in the desert'" (Ex 14:11).

Yahweh had never mentioned it would be like this. Opposition from Pharaoh Moses could understand. But he has to learn the hard way that captives have to be ransomed. They are rarely willing to pay their own way. Externally the crowd is at least dragging its feet in the right direction. But interior liberation, freedom of the spirit, is not even on the map. Even for Moses, the fire in his heart can stand just so much cold water. For him, too, liberation is a process, not an unforgettable moment. For him it will be complete only when he dies in peace—on the wrong side of the boundary of the Promised Land.

There is "one brief, and shining moment" when Moses and his people stand together in a burst of jubilation. On the other side of the Sea of Reeds, they are well out of Pharaoh's reach. For the whole crowd, there is a triumphant feeling, which they express in the beautiful Song of Miriam. But as they enter their own desert, they take with them all their fears and insecurities, their shortsightedness and lack of understanding of what it is all about. They continue their grumbling mistrust of Moses. They idealize the past, longing for the fleshpots and forgetting the slave drivers. They make the entire journey as a disgruntled group of spoiled children who step out of character only occasionally. They are beautiful at Sinai, but the covenant soon lies in shambles at the feet of a golden calf. It will have to be renewed over and over again in the long tradition that began when Moses took his shoes off.

Freedom in Tension

The radical transformation of Moses places him squarely in the middle of a constant dialectic between God and his people. He is not simply a mouthpiece on behalf of either because his heart is invested in both. He is so one with the heart of Yahweh that when he speaks to the people he can declare, "Yahweh says." He is so one with the fragile people that when he speaks to Yahweh, he cannot always say, "Thy will be done." Often he pleads, "Thy will be changed." For example, after the golden calf incident, "Yahweh said to Moses, 'I can see how stiff-necked these people are. Let me alone, then, that my wrath may blaze out against them and devour them'" (Ex 32:10). It is as though Yahweh admits his own weakness in the face of Moses, whose prayer he knows will touch his heart. Moses approaches Yahweh with the heart of his people. He pleads for mercy like a skilled advocate and ends with: "Leave your burning wrath; relent and do not bring disaster on your people" (Ex 32:12). "So Yahweh relented," we are told, "and did not bring on his people the disaster he threatened" (Ex 32:14).

Moses Unbound

There is no evidence of selfishness left in the truly free Moses. He belongs to Yahweh and to his people. No matter what the cost, he will not give up on either. He embodies the greatest and the first commandment, as well as the second, which is inseparable from it. The final evidence of his inner liberation is his unquestioning acceptance of the heavy sentence Yahweh has laid on him alone for a momentary infidelity. Yahweh said to him:

> "Climb Mount Nebo…and view the land of Canaan which I am giving the children of Israel as their domain. Die on the mountain you have climbed and be gathered to your people.…Because you broke faith with me once that time at Meribath Kadesh, because you did not display my holiness among the children of Israel, you may see this land only from afar; you cannot enter it, this land I am giving to the children of Israel." (Dt 32:49-52)

In response, Moses gives his farewell blessing to the rarely faithful tribes of Israel. Externally, he dies in failure, as so many other prophets must do, just outside the Promised Land. But the inner man has made it well across the line.

Moses was admittedly a most unusual man. But there is a Moses in each of us who at times strikes out in anger at a manifest injustice and is ready to take on the powers of darkness single-handedly; who at the time sneaks off to a Midian to save his own skin, but who also is capable of one day seeing a bush on fire and knowing that it mirrors his own heart. Once this happens, the Moses in us will know it is time to bring the burning message to everyone that we can reach. And the message? The precious name: "I will be there, as who I am, I will be there."

From: *The Bible Today,* January 1981

9. CREATION MYTHS FROM OTHER CULTURES

Dog was going around with Creator. Everywhere he went, Dog went, and watched all that he did. When Creator finished one job and moved on to another, the dog went too.

"Are you going to stay around here all the time?" said the dog. "Or will you have to go away?"

"Well, perhaps someday I shall have to live far away," said the Creator.

"Then, Grandfather, will you make me a companion?" So the Creator lay down on the ground.

"Draw a line around me with your paw," he said. So Dog scratched an outline in the earth all around the great Creator. Creator got up and looked at it.

"Go a little way off and don't look," he said. The dog went off a little way. In a few minutes he looked.

"Oh, someone is lying where you were lying, Grandfather."

"Go along and don't look," he said. The dog went off a little way. In a few minutes he looked.

"Someone is sitting there, Grandfather," he said.

"Turn around and walk farther off," said the Creator. The dog obeyed. At last Creator called the dog. "Now you can look," he said.

"Oh, Grandfather, he moves," cried the dog in delight. So they stood by the man and looked him over.

"Pretty good," said the Creator.

"He's wonderful," said the dog.

Creator went behind the man and lifted him to his feet. "Put out your foot," he said. "Walk, do this." So the man walked.

"Now run," Creator said. He took hold of the man and showed him how to run. The man ran.

"Talk," said the Creator. But the man said nothing. Four times Creator told the man to talk. "Say words," he said. Finally the man said words. He spoke.

"Now shout," said Creator. He gave a big yell himself and showed the man how. The man shouted.

"What else?" the man said.

Creator thought a minute, "Laugh," he said. "Laugh, laugh, laugh."

Then the man laughed.

The dog was very happy when the man laughed. He jumped up on him and ran off a little, and ran back and jumped up on him. He kept jumping up on him the way dogs do today when they are full of love and delight. The man laughed and laughed.

"Now you are fit to live," said Creator. So the man went off with his dog.

— Jicarilla Apache Indians

The creator Juok molded all men of earth, and while he was engaged in the work of creation he wandered about the world.

In the land of the whites he found a pure white earth or sand; and out of it he shaped white men. Then he came to the land of Egypt and out of the mud of the Nile he made red or brown men. Lastly, he came to the land of the Shilluks, and finding there black earth he created black men out of it.

The way in which he modeled men was this. He took a lump of earth and said to himself, "I will make man, but he must be able to walk and run and go out into the fields, so I will give him two long legs, like the flamingo."

Having done so, he thought again, "The man must be able to cultivate his millet, so I will give him two arms, one to hold the hoe, and the other to tear up the weeds." So he gave him two arms.

Then he thought again, and he said to himself, "The man must be able to see his millet, so I will give him two eyes." He did so accordingly.

Next he thought to himself, "The man must

be able to eat his millet, so I will give him a mouth." And a mouth he gave him accordingly.

After that he thought within himself, "The man must be able to dance and speak and sing and shout, and for these purposes he must have a tongue." And a tongue he gave him accordingly.

Lastly, the deity said to himself, "The man must be able to hear the noise of the dance and the speech of the great men, and for that he needs two ears." So two ears he gave him, and sent him out into the world a perfect man.

— Shilluk Tribe of Africa

Earthmaker made man out of a little piece of earth and shaped it like himself. Then he spoke to man, but the man did not answer. He did not hear. So Earthmaker put his finger into his own right ear, and then into the ear of the man. Then he spoke to the man again. The man could hear, but did not answer. He could not see. So Earthmaker touched his own eyes, then the eyes of the man, and the man could see.

Earthmaker spoke to him again, but still the man did not speak. So he put his fingers on his own lips and then touched the lips of the man. The man could speak, but he did not know what to say. Earthmaker then perceived that the man had neither mind nor heart. So he breathed his own breath into the mouth of the man, and the man breathed and his heart was full.

Earthmaker spoke to the man again and the man answered his creator; very nicely and quietly he answered.

Earthmaker then sent the man into the world.

— Winnabago Indians

In the beginning, at all times, above the earth, in this place, Upon the earth there was a huge mist, and there was the Great Manito.

In the beginning, for ever, lost in space, was the Great Manito.

He made the huge earth and the sky.

He made the sun, the moon, and the stars.

He made everything move in harmony.

Then the wind blew violently, it became lighter and lighter, and water flowed strongly and from afar.

And groups of islands emerged and remained.

Once again, the Great Manito spoke, one Manito to other Manitos.

To mortal creatures, spirits and all.

And thereafter he was the Manito of men, and their grandfather.

He sent the first mother, the mother of all creatures.

He sent fish, he sent turtles, he sent wild beasts, he sent birds.

But a spiteful Manito made only spiteful creatures, monsters.

He made flies, he made mosquitoes.

All creatures were friendly with one another at that time.

Truly the Manitos were very active and considerate.

To these first men of all and to these first mothers of all:

    they found them spouses.

And they gave them to eat when they needed to.

And all possessed joyful wisdom, and had time to spare and happiness.

— from the *Walam Olum* or Red Book of The Lenape or Delaware Indians

The Old Man above did not use earth and sticks to make men. He simply thought, and there they were.

— Wijot Indians

10. THE YAHWIST PASSAGES FROM THE PENTATEUCH

from *The Yahwist, The Bible's First Theologian*

by Peter Ellis

PART I—THE PRIMEVAL HISTORY

The Yahwist's primeval history has been amalgamated in Genesis 1–11 with the Priestly source by the final editor of the Pentateuch. Out of approximately 300 verses in Genesis 1–11, roughly 150 belong to the Yahwist and 150 to the Priestly source. The following pericopes are generally credited to the Yahwist:

Paradise	Gn	2:4b–25
The Fall		3:1–24
Cain and Abel		4:1–16
The descendants of Cain		4:17–24
The descendants of Seth		4:25–26
Sons of god and the daughters of men		6:1–4
The corruption of mankind		6:5–8
Preparations for the flood		7:1–10, 12, 16b
The flood		7:17a, 22–23
The flood subsides		8:3, 6, 8–13, 20–22
Noah and his sons		9:18–27
Genealogies		10:8–19, 21, 24–30
The tower of Babel		11:1–9
The descendants of Terah		11:28–30

PART II—THE PATRIARCHAL HISTORY

The patriarchal history in Genesis 12–50 contains materials from three sources: the Yahwist's saga, the Elohist's saga, and the Priestly source. Out of approximately 1300 verses in Genesis 12–50, roughly 800 belong to the Yahwist; 300 to the Elohist; and 200 to the Priestly source. The following pericopes are generally credited to the Yahwist:

The Story of Abraham

The call of Abraham	12:1–3, 4a, 6–9
Abraham in Egypt	12:10–20
Abraham and Lot separate	13:1–5, 7–11, 13–18
The campaign of the four great kings	14:1–16
Melchizedek	14:17–24
The divine promises and covenant	15:1–4, 6–12, 17–21
The birth of Ishmael	16:1–2, 3b–14
The apparition at Mamre	18:1–33
The destruction of Sodom	19:1–29
The origin of the Moabites and Ammonites	19:30–38
The birth of Isaac	21:1–2a, 6–7, 33
The sacrifice of Isaac	22:1–19
The descendants of Nahor	22:20–24
The tomb of the patriarchs	23:2–20
The marriage of Isaac	24:1–67
The descendants of Keturah	25:1–6,11b

The Story of Isaac and Jacob

The birth of Esau and Jacob	25:21–28
Esau gives up his birthright	25:29–34
Isaac at Gerar	26:1–14
The wells between Gerar and Beersheba	26:15–25
The alliance with Abimelech	26:26–33
Jacob obtains Isaac's blessing by cunning	27:1–45
Jacob's dream	28:10–11a, 13–16, 19
Jacob arrives at Laban's home	29:1–14a
Jacob's two marriages	29:15–30
The sons of Jacob	29:31–35, 30:3–5, 7–16, 21, 24

How Jacob became rich	30:25-43
Jacob's flight	31:1-21
Laban pursues Jacob	31:22-42
A treaty between Jacob and Laban	31:43-54
Jacob prepares for his meeting with Esau	32:3-22
Jacob wrestles with God	32:23-33
The meeting with Esau	33:1-11
Jacob leaves Esau	33:17
The rape of Dinah	34:1-5
The matrimonial alliance with the Shechemites	34:6-24
The treacherous revenge of Simeon and Levi	34:25-31
Reuben's incest	35:21-22

The Story of Joseph

Joseph and his brothers	37:2b-11
Joseph sold by his brothers	37:12-20, 25-27, 28b
The story of Judah and Tamar	38:1-30
Joseph's early days in Egypt	39:1-6
The attempt to seduce Joseph	39:7-20
Joseph in gaol	39:21-23
Jacob's sons return to Canaan	42:26-28
Jacob's sons leave again with Benjamin	43:1-14
The meeting with Joseph	43:15-34
Joseph's cup in Benjamin's sack	44:1-17
Judah intervenes	44:18-34
Joseph makes himself known	45:1-15
Pharaoh's invitation	45:16-20
The return to Canaan	45:21-28
Jacob leaves for Egypt	46:1
Joseph welcomes them	46:28-34
Pharaoh grants an audience	47:1-6
Joseph's agrarian policy	47:13-26
Jacob's last wishes	47:27a, 29-31
Jacob adopts Joseph's two sons and blesses them	48:8-22
Jacob's blessings	49:2-28
Jacob's funeral	50:1-11, 14

PART III—THE NATIONAL HISTORY

The national history, relating the events that went into the birth of Israel as God's chosen nation, is broken up into two sections by extensive interpolations of Priestly material. The first section in Exodus 1-24; 32-34 is separated from the last section in Numbers 10-24 by the huge liturgical corpus of the Priestly source interpolated after Exodus 24.

Both in Exodus 1-24; 32-33 and Numbers 10-24 there is an admixture of material from the Yahwist, the Elohist, and the Priestly source. Out of approximately 1200 verses in both sections, roughly 600 come from the Yahwist. The distribution of source material is more difficult and more debatable than the distribution in Genesis, principally because so much of the Exodus story has been taken from liturgical complexes. Nevertheless, the following pericopes in Exodus and Numbers can be attributed with good probability to the Yahwist:

The Hebrews oppressed	Ex 1:8-12, 22
The birth of Moses	2:1-10
Moses escapes to Midian	2:11-22
The burning bush	3:2-4, 7-8
Moses instructed for his mission	3:16-20
Moses granted miraculous powers	4:1, 5-7
Aaron, the mouthpiece of Moses	4:10-14
Moses returns to Egypt. He leaves Midian	4:18-20a
The son of Moses circumcised	4:24-26
Moses meets Aaron	4:27-31
The first audience with Pharaoh	5:1-5
Instruction to the slave-drivers	5:6-14
The Hebrew foremen complain	5:15-18
The dilemma of the foremen. Moses prays	5:19-6:1
The water turns to blood	7:14-17, 21, 23-25
The frogs	7:26-29; 8:1-15
The gadflies	8:16-32
Death of the Egyptians' livestock	9:1-7

The hail	9:13, 17–18, 23b, 24b, 25b–26, 28–29, 33–35	Moses' proposal to Hobab	Nm 10:29–32
		The departure	10:33–36
The locusts	10:3–7, 12a, 13b, 14b, 16a, 17–19	**The Halts in the Wilderness**	
		Taberah	11:1–3
The darkness	10:21–29	Kibroth-hattaavah.	
Moses proclaims the		The people complain	11:4–9
death of the firstborn	11:4–8	The prayer of Moses	11:10–15
Injunctions relating to the Passover	12:21–23	Yahweh replies	11:16–23
Death of the firstborn	12:29–31	The spirit given to the elders	11:24–30
Israel's departure	12:27a, 28–39; 13:20–22	The quails	11:31–35
		Hazeroth. Complaints of	
The Egyptians pursue the Israelites	14:5–7, 10, 13–14	Miriam and Aaron	12:1–3
		God's answer	12:4–10
The crossing	14:19b–21, 24–25, 27, 30–31	The prayer of Aaron and Moses	12:11–16
		The reconnaissance in Canaan	13:17–24
Song of victory	15:1–19	The envoys' report	13:26–31, 32b–33
		The rebellion of Israel	14:1, 4
Israel in the Desert		The anger of Yahweh. Moses	
Marah	15:22–25	makes an appeal	14:11–19
The manna	16:4–5, 28–31, 35	Pardon and punishment	14:20–25
		An abortive attempt by the Israelites	14:39–45
The water from the rock	17:1–7	The rebellion of Dathan and Abiram	16:1b, 2a, 12–15
A battle against the Amalekites	17:8–16	The punishment	16:25–26, 27b–32a, 33–34a
The Covenant at Sinai			
The Israelites come to Sinai	19:2b	**From Kadesh to Moab**	
Preparing for the Covenant	19:10–11, 13b, 14–15	Edom refuses right of way	20:1b, 14–21
		The capture of Hormah	21:1–3
The theophany on Sinai	19:16–20a	The bronze serpent	21:5–9
Moses on the mountain	24:12–15	By stages to Transjordania	21:12–20
The golden calf	32:1–6	The conquest of Transjordania	21:21–22:1
Moses forewarned by Yahweh	32:7a, 8–10	The king of Moab appeals	
The prayer of Moses	32:11–14	to Balaam	22:5–8, 13–19, 21
Moses breaks the tablets of the Law	32:15–24	Balaam's donkey	22:22–35
The zeal of the Levites	32:25–29	Balaam and Balak	22:36–38;
The Israelites ordered to depart	33:1, 2b, 3–4		24:2–25
Moses prays	33:12–17		
The Covenant renewed.			
The tablets of the Law	34:1–5		
The Covenant	34:10, 14–28		

11. FATHER ABRAHAM, MY FRIEND AND MENTOR

By Jean Jeffrey Gietzen

Webster defines a mentor as a wise and trusted teacher, a guide, and a friend. In my lifetime, I have had many mentors—those college teachers who taught me to think; my first boss, who guided me through the steps of magazine editing; and friends old and young who taught me the skills of motherhood and homemaking.

One particular mentor was a young priest whose enthusiasm for Scripture was as catching as a virus. It was he who led me to my dear friend and spiritual mentor, Abraham. For the past several years, I have been on the Genesis journey with Abraham. I invite you to come along and travel with us in faith.

Abraham's journey

Our travels begin in Genesis 12. The author of this section tells us that the Lord called Abraham to leave the land of Ur: "The Lord said to Abram: 'Go forth from the land of your kinsfolk and from your father's house to a land that I will show you,'" and later that "Abram went as the Lord directed him, and Lot went with him" (Gn 12:1-4).

As I look back over my life, I see that the Lord has called me too, directing my steps, leading me from one stage of faith to another. When I walk in complete trust, I know that no harm shall come to me.

Abraham was so convinced that God was with him each step of the way that he stopped often to build an altar in praise of his God. If I do not rush through each day in a frenzy of activity, I too can take time out for prayer and praise.

Link with yesterday

In this same chapter we learn that Abraham took all of his possessions with him when he left his homeland. I see those possessions as his link to the past, his way of remembering those who had given him life and prepared him to be ready when the Lord called him.

As I walk along with Abraham on my journey of faith, I often remember to say a little prayer of thanks for those people who first set me on the path of faith, my parents and godparents. How grateful I am for their presence in my life. Without them, I would not have known the Lord. They readied me to respond to the Lord at all the various stages of my life. Even now, my parents' letters create a bond of trust and faith that cannot be broken.

Just when I'm sitting comfortably in the shade of complacency, God might intervene and open up a new avenue of faith.

Obstacles to love

Abraham's journey was not without its problems. In chapter 13, he finds that the land cannot support both his family and Lot's. After spending time in prayer, Abraham discusses the problem with Lot. The two men agree to part ways.

There have been times in my life when I recognized that a particular activity or friendship was robbing my family of my time and energy. I pulled back, chose a different direction or way of being— and found the Lord with me in my decision. I see this happening now with my older children as my husband and I struggle with their need to be independent and our fears that they might not be ready for the world beyond our love.

Yes, Abraham's dialogue with Lot in this chapter is much like the dialogue between parent and young adult. And look! There at the end of the chapter, Abraham again finds time to build an altar to the Lord, who has been with him in this latest struggle just as he promised.

Dialogue with the Lord

As a child, my faith life was a simple matter. I did exactly what was expected of me with no questions asked. My father encouraged me to just bow my head and accept those things about my faith that were a mystery. As an adult, I have learned to dialogue with God in much the same way as Abraham does in Genesis 18:16-33.

When Abraham asks the Lord over and over again how many innocent people must be in the city so the Lord will not destroy it, I sense that Abraham is really saying, "What are you like, God? How much can you do? Do you care for your people as deeply as I believe you do? Will you always be with me or will you one day turn your back on me?"

When I begin to question, to struggle with my faith, I know it is time to seek answers, to get help, to reconcile myself once more to the Lord. Our parish offers many ways to deal with the struggle. I can visit the sick and elderly in my parish, I can offer my time as a lay minister of the Word, I can say "yes" more often than "no." I can learn to see requests for help as a call from the Lord—and I can respond positively if I know my talents could serve him.

God of surprises

On my journey with Abraham, I have learned to expect the unexpected. When Abraham was seventy-five, God promised he would be the father of many. God does not fulfill that promise until Abraham is ninety-nine.

Chapter 21 helps me to see that it could be a newcomer to my community who might lead me to a deeper understanding of what it means to be a person of faith and trust.

Just when I'm sitting comfortably in the shade of complacency, God might intervene and open up a new avenue of faith. He has already

done so in my lifetime with the challenge of Vatican II. What more does the Lord have in mind for me on my journey? He has blessed me by friends, shared his creative powers with me so that I might bring children into the world.

This God of surprises is the same God who walked and talked with Abraham. When I set off each day on my journey of faith, he is with me too.

God of reconciliation

Abraham's faith and trust in God is tested in chapter 22, in the story of the near-sacrifice of Isaac, Abraham's only child. This chapter has always presented problems for me. How could God ask Abraham to slaughter the son he loves, the hope for the future of Israel?

But then, how often do I slaughter those I love with unkind words, with cold silences, my inability to listen? How often have I refused to say "I love you" when I know that is what a spouse, child, or friend needs to hear?

I read those verses now as an examination of conscience and pray that God will point out to me, as he did to Abraham, a way out of my indifference.

The succeeding verses help me to recognize God's saving grace. The words, "Do not lay your hand on the boy," caution me to be more gentle with those I love. There are times, after a particularly beautiful reconciliation service, when I have been tempted to name the place of reconciliation *Yahweh-Yireh*, a Hebrew expression meaning "the Lord will see to it." *Yahweh-Yireh* is the name Abraham gives to the place where God saved him from destroying his beloved son (Gn 22:1-14).

Angels of my own

Reading all of chapter 22, I feel a touch of longing to ask those I love to forgive my insensitivities toward them and beg their blessing. Abraham is blessed abundantly by angels and messengers of God as he makes his way in faith. My friends and loved ones are twentieth-century angels and messengers of the Lord.

At the end of his life, Abraham deeds all that he has to his son Isaac. His "all" is what he has learned on his journey. I want to be able to pass on my relationship with God, complete and gift-wrapped, to those who come after me. But that is not the way of a friend of Abraham's. A friend of Abraham's will only point out the way, mention there might be detours, and trust that those of the next generation will make their own faith-journey. God himself will lead them.

Abraham and you

If you would like to know more about my friend and mentor Abraham, read chapters 12 through 25 of the Book of Genesis. As you read, ask yourself these questions:

Do I go as the Lord directs me in my faith life or do I hold back?

Do I cling tightly to the past, unwilling to believe that where I am now is exactly where God intends me to be?

Do I pray for those who first set me on the road of faith? Do I seek out activities and people who can help me grow?

Do I wait for a personal visit from the priests in my parish before I respond to the call of the Lord? Do I see the Lord in the strangers in my midst?

Have I told my family and friends that I love them and value our relationship, or do I find myself threatening these relationships with silence, a cold shoulder, or a refusal to listen to their point of view?

Do I see how often God has called me to reconciliation and I have refused to respond?

Am I willing to trust the Lord as he leads my children and grandchildren into the twenty-first century surrounded with his love and care?

Do I believe that the God who walked and talked with Abraham, walked with my own mother and father in the cool of the evening and surprised them with the unexpectedness of his constancy?

Do I believe that this same God will continue to surprise me on my own ever-changing journey of faith even until my dying day?

When you travel with Abraham as your guide and mentor, be prepared to laugh, to cry, to part with those who rob you of energy, to accept change, to welcome the Lord in strangers, and to remember that no matter how difficult the journey, God will lead you.

Go then as the Lord directs you—and may you find peace and joy on your way.

From: *Liguorian*, April 1984

Genesis 18:2 "He saw three men standing"

12. ON BURYING OUR ISAACS

By Mary Catherine Barron, C.S.J.

The word of God is something alive and active; it cuts like any double-edged sword but more finely; it can slip through the place where the soul is divided from the spirit, or joints from the marrow; it can judge the secret emotions and thoughts. No created thing can hide from him; everything is uncovered and open to the eyes of the one to whom we must give an account of ourselves. (Heb 4:12-13)

It happened some time later that God put Abraham to the test. (Gn 22:1)

Abraham was a vulnerable man. He could never quite master the art of resisting God. Always, he was too available. Had he been a more pragmatic human being, he would have quickly cultivated a quality of deafness where God was concerned—or at least a fair pretense of it. But that was his weakness: he was too receptive. Whenever God called, he answered. Such alacrity can be dangerous, especially where Yahweh is involved. He is all-consuming.

And so when, after a short span of years of relative peace and quiet, God once again cried out his name: "Abraham, Abraham," our Old Testament forefather responded as could be expected: "Here I am." He should have known better. He should have realized the incipient danger of those words, because he had uttered them before and they had cost him quite a bit of pain. In fact, they had brought him to where he was then: in a strange land of strange people with a young son, the fruit of his and Sarah's old age. It had been a weary journey to this destination, filled with suffering and hope, alienation and promise, discouragement and fulfillment. But today, existence was peaceful and God was benign and Abraham was happy in the new life

growing up around him: Isaac, his son. So he never should have answered with such openness, such literalness, when he said: "Here I am." Those three words capsulized a whole lifetime of givenness and surrender on Abraham's part and God knew that. He knew the implied depths of Abraham's response because long ago he had blasted his foundation, carved him out, and molded him in faith. So God was not surprised at Abraham's reply. He had tested him before.

Purgation is a messy business. No matter how finely wrought the instrument, there is always pain and a certain amount of blood-letting. Ironically, although we are quite familiar with the concept, we are never much at ease in the throes of the process. Double-edged swords are dangerous, especially the ones that slip into the hidden place "where the soul is divided from the spirit," because eventually they strike the heart. Abraham had been prodded and probed before. But he had also lived long enough to realize that there are always untouched recesses, crevices of the heart, where the finger of God has not yet been felt.

One of those crevices contained Isaac. And so Yahweh commands: "Take your son, your only child Isaac, whom you love, and go to the land of Moriah. There you shall offer him as a burnt offering, on a mountain I will point out to you" (Gn 22:2). God couldn't have been more blunt nor, apparently, more unfeeling. With near ferocity, he highlights the very nadir points involved in Abraham's sacrifice: "son," "only child," "Isaac," "whom you love." And then he conjures up a picture of that supple-limbed first fruit of endless expectation: blackened—a burnt offering on a wilderness mountaintop.

Abraham makes no response because he has already made the total one of "Here I am." We are simply told that early next morning he rises and begins the three days' journey to Moriah. Whatever the outcome, the journey itself is part of the purgation, is already a piece of the burnt offering, and the fact that it is leading to final consummation only intensifies the pain.

Anguish is not a very communicable emotion. It is too deep for utterance. So insistent is it that all other feelings give way before its flood. So Abraham says little on the pilgrimage to holocaust, but in grim irony loads Isaac with the wood and himself takes the knife and the fire. In stolid faith, Abraham bears in his own hands the purgative instruments that will cut and sear his son. But more deeply, he bears the instruments that will cut and sear *himself*. Isaac is to suffer a holocaust of body; Abraham suffers a holocaust of heart.

Outrage always accompanies the destruction of an innocent—outrage on the part of the nonparticipants. But who can fathom the outrage Abraham feels as he blinds his only son and lays him on the altar? We cannot begin to plumb the depths of his grieving heart that still believes in the irrevocable word of Yahweh. "Abraham stretched out his hand and seized the knife to kill his son" (Gn 22:10).

Once again the cry comes: "Abraham, Abraham," and once again the familiar response is given: "I am here." And then come the salvific words: "Do not raise your hand against the boy; do not harm him, for now I know you fear God. You have not refused me your son, your only son" (Gn 22:11–13). Isaac is spared. What about Abraham? The holocaust of the body does not occur; the holocaust of the heart is complete.

Father van Breemen in his book *Called By Name* offers the following analysis:

> When Abraham descends from the mountain with his son, both he and Isaac have changed; something has happened on that hilltop.... Like a tree which has been turned full circle in the ground, Abraham's roots have been cut loose, and he has returned a new man. (p.19)

In what does his newness consist? Abraham comes down the mountain with a living Isaac. Yet something in both of them is dead. Because he was bent over the prone Isaac on the altar, we could not see the pain in Abraham's eyes, the look of utter bewilderment at what he was about to do, the trembling terror at the death of love by his own hand. But Isaac could see. And in that look of love that was exchanged between them—father and son—the holocaust of the heart is accomplished. In that instant, Isaac cedes over his life to his father in trust and surrender. And Abraham cedes over his heart to Yahweh in a similar fashion. Because part of Abraham's heart is Isaac, that part of Isaac in Abraham's heart dies forever on Mount Moriah. Abraham returns to Beersheba with a son, but no longer with *his* son. Isaac is irrevocably gone, yielded over to Yahweh. Isaac returns with a father who is no longer solely *his* father, but more radically is father to Yahweh's people. Both lose and gain life; both surrender the other and are given the other in return—but transformed.

In the Letter to the Hebrews we are told:

> It was by faith that Abraham, when put to the test, offered up Isaac. He offered to sacrifice his only son even though the promises had been made to him and he had been told: It is through Isaac that your name will be carried on. He was confident that God had the power to raise the dead; and so, figuratively speaking, he was given back Isaac from the dead. (Heb 11:17-19)

Centuries later, when speaking of losing and gaining life, Jesus would use the analogy of the wheat grain dying in the earth to produce a rich harvest. We might say that out of the seed of love for Isaac, which Abraham allows to die in the holy ground of Yahweh, comes the rich harvest of transformed life. For Abraham, indeed, has Isaac back from the dead, but only after he has first let him go. In a sense, he leaves Mount Moriah having buried part of himself and his son there.

So what does the story mean to us? Certainly we are relieved that Isaac is not slain. We are glad that Abraham's faith was vindicated. And we hope that we are never put to such a test. It is just such a latter mentality that is our mistake and our misfortune. For we all have our Isaacs—those hidden crevices of the heart where we do not even realize that "the soul is divided from the spirit." Unless we are willing to bury them (our Isaacs) in a holocaust of the heart, our faith is weak and our love is unfree. And to that extent we are poor spiritual progeny of our great desert patriarch.

The book of Judith tells us:

> We should be grateful to the Lord our God, for putting us to the test, as he did our forefathers. Recall how he dealt with Abraham, and how he tried Isaac, and all that happened to Jacob in Syrian Mesopotamia while he was tending the flocks of Laban, his mother's brother. Not for vengeance did the Lord put them in the crucible to try their hearts, nor has he done so with us. It is by way of admonition that he chastises those who are close to him. (8:25-27)

Admonition for what? Admonition, so that eventually our hearts in the crucible will be so totally purified that we will, indeed, have laid to final rest all our Isaacs. Admonition, so that eventually our hearts in the crucible will be so totally free that we too will be able to respond as did Abraham to Yahweh's call: "Here I am."

"The word of God is something alive and active"—in Abraham's day and in our own. Will we let it pierce us, double-edged though it might be?

From: *Unveiled Faces: Men and Women of the Bible,* by Mary Catherine Barron, C.S.J.

The art of being wise is the art of knowing what to overlook.

— William James

13. BIBLICAL HEROES AND THEIR JOURNEYS OF FAITH

From Abraham to Jesus

by Sr. Macrina Scott, O.S.F.

A wise way for us to approach the Messiah born at Bethlehem is to walk in the faith of his forebears and travel the biblical landscape from which he emerged. In this article therefore, we go back and examine the faith of Abraham and of other great biblical figures who preceded Jesus. Their journeys shed light on our own.

It all began with Abraham

During the 18th century before Christ, a nomad lived in his tent near the great city of Haran, much as the Bedouin live in their tents in Israel today, outsiders, living a primitive life-style on the periphery of a highly developed civilization. The Bible tells us nothing that indicates this man was different from other inhabitants of the desert, the Third World of his day. If he were exceptionally wise or exceptionally virtuous, that fact has not been preserved for us. What has been preserved is that God spoke to him. As far as we know, it is the first time that God chooses to break through the infinite distance that separates Creator from creation to begin a conversation with humankind. It is the beginning of the journey.

What God says to Abraham is a terrible command: "Leave your family and your homeland, everything that is familiar and secure, and set out on a journey." To make the uprooting more difficult, he is not even told the goal of the journey. "Go to a land that I *will* show you."

Abraham is the model of faith for all who hear the Lord calling us to leave behind the world to which we are accustomed and to move in a direction that is new and untried.

Mother Teresa heard that call when she left the form of religious life to which she was accustomed, to begin a new kind of ministry among the outcasts of Calcutta. Franciscan Father Maximilian Kolbe heard it in a Nazi concentration camp when he stepped out from the relative safety of a group of prisoners to volunteer to replace a fellow prisoner condemned to death. Today religious groups involved in the sanctuary movement are leaving behind the cooperation between Church and state, which has become traditional in our country, to confront the state on the matter of granting asylum to refugees. Individual workers are leaving secure jobs, for reasons of conscience, to face the possibility of long-term unemployment.

At the Second Vatican Council the Church as a whole responded to a call to leave behind much that was familiar and seemed secure, to open up new paths, the ends of which no one could see. We are an Abraham people.

Propelled by God's promise

What gives Abraham the courage to make the leap of faith? Unlike later generations, he has no past experience of God to give him confidence. All God gives him is a promise of the two things for which his heart longs. At the age of 75 Abraham has had no son, a great disaster at a time when people believed that the only way in which they could live on after death was in their children. And he has no land. Like all nomads, he lives on the fringes of the rich earth that bears crops. He lives on the dry wasteland, which can only feed his flocks for a while; then he has to move to another spot. He admires the wealth, ease and rootedness of his landed neighbors just as Third World people today admire the living standards of the First World.

God promises this nomad "as many descendants as the stars in the heavens" and a land of his own—big promises from a new and untried God. The marvelous thing about Abraham is that he is able to believe.

There is a third promise, too. Perhaps it is of more interest to us than to Abraham. This is a promise that through him, insignificant citizen of the Third World, all the nations of the world will somehow be blessed. Through the risky journey that he is about to begin, Abraham will serve the saving plan of God of which he has only the faintest glimmer of understanding.

Abraham lives by faith

Abraham had been born in Ur, near the River Euphrates, where so many of the great civilizations of the Ancient Near East developed. He had moved with his father to Haran, far north but near the same Euphrates River. When he leaves Haran, he travels to Canaan. He stops first at Shechem.

At Shechem God speaks to Abraham again. Now that he has left everything behind and brought his family on this great journey, God repeats the promise of blessings, and adds a new piece of information. *"This* is the land I will give you." It is still only a promise. The Canaanites are in possession of the land, and Abraham only wanders on the outskirts of their cities as he had at Ur and Haran. (The only land he would ever possess is a field near Hebron which he purchases to bury his wife Sarah.) But he lives by faith in the promise, and the promise is now attached to a concrete bit of this earth. He will travel far away from it, but his hope is based on it, like his descendants' hope for nearly 4,000 years. It is often hard for those who are not Jewish to understand the obsession of their Zionist friends with this unlikely bit of land. But its roots go back to Abraham.

Abraham has arrived at the land of promise, but after some time famine hits the land, and he is forced to travel with his family to Egypt, the other center of civilization in the Ancient Near East. The mighty River Nile makes Egypt the breadbasket of the ancient world. Our father Abraham is probably dazzled by the wealth and culture of

Egypt, as Third World visitors can be dazzled by what they see in the United States. The Pyramids are already hundreds of years old, a witness to the hungry nomad Abraham of the great power and venerable traditions of Egypt.

Tests along the way

The strongest feeling of the little band of nomads in this foreign land is probably fear, a fear much like that experienced by refugees newly arrived in America. Abraham's fear is heightened when he sees that Pharaoh is attracted by the beautiful Sarah. There is nothing to prevent the all-powerful Pharaoh from killing the newcomers and taking Sarah.

Pressured by that fear, Abraham presents Sarah as his sister, to allow Pharaoh to add her to his harem. We see a similar thing today. People of the Third World become so frightened by our military and economic power that they are tempted to sacrifice their values to buy our protection as Abraham sacrificed Sarah.

Perhaps Abraham has forgotten the promise of possessing his own land, especially since there has been no sign of fulfillment of the all-important promise that he would have descendants to inherit the Promised Land. But God has not forgotten the promise. And the promise applies not to Abraham alone, but to his wife Sarah as well. Abraham could have children by other women, and he does, but they do not inherit the promise. Only through the child of Sarah can the journey be continued. God may have been as disappointed with Abraham as Abraham was with God. At this moment of crisis, when the whole future was endangered by Sarah's being taken into Pharaoh's harem, God does not speak to Abraham, but to Pharaoh, warning him to return Sarah to her embarrassed husband.

Lessons for us

Abraham's Egypt experience has a message for our era, too. Egypt represents those points on our journey where God's promise seems far away and unfulfilling, and the pressures of the world immediately around us are powerful and frightening. Then we are tempted to sell part of ourselves, to sacrifice our wholeness to the powers of this world in exchange for the security they offer us. It can happen at such a time that God uses the very powers of this world to disillusion us, and send us back to the journey to which we are called, as God sent Abraham back through Pharaoh.

Sarah and Abraham are put out of Egypt by the indignant Pharaoh. They return to the Promised Land, and wander from end to end of it, as if every part of the land had first to be blessed by this old nomad's footprints before his descendants could claim it as their own, build houses and plant crops.

In every age, including our own, there are people who have the call Abraham and Sarah had: to open new paths, to prepare the way for those who will come in future generations, never to settle down and take possession of a land. These are the pioneers, the trailblazers. Only in future generations does their work take on meaning. Charles de Foucauld and Teilhard de Chardin were such figures; perhaps there are others among us whom we do not recognize.

Difficult things can be asked of those on a journey. When at last Abraham receives the precious beginning of the fulfillment of the promises, his son Isaac, he has to show his willingness to sacrifice even that great gift. He knows the pain of every parent who, in one way or another, has to let go of a dearly loved child. When Abraham dies, his body is placed next to that of Sarah in the burial ground he purchased near Hebron, a silent witness to his faith that one day the whole land will belong to his descendants. But the journey continues.

Isaac: a milder journeyer

Isaac, the rather colorless son of the promise, is content to continue his father's journey back and forth, over every part of the land that was one day to belong to his descendants. He stretches the area a bit, spending considerable time around Beersheba, the traditional southern border of the Promised Land. Even today Beersheba primarily is a center for the numerous Bedouin who still follow the nomadic life-style—much like Abraham and Isaac—though today one is likely to see television antennae protruding out of their tents.

There are people and generations like Isaac, content to follow in the footsteps of their parents, making only minor steps forward on the journey. But it is not for us to condemn pilgrims who are less daring, but faithful to the Lord of the journey.

Jacob: a model for strugglers

Isaac's son, Jacob, is the opposite of his father. If there is trouble to be found, he will find it. As a young man, he so angers his brother Esau that he has to leave the country to escape Esau's righteous wrath. Where is he to go at such a time?

He returns to Haran, where his grandfather began the journey of faith. But he too has heard the voice of God promising him the land of Canaan first promised to his grandfather Abraham. So when he finds himself in trouble with his father-in-law in Haran, he returns with his family to that land which draws him like a magnet.

Jacob's struggles give contemporary believers food for thought. Many today make similar excursions in the course of our journey of faith. It can happen that at a time of crisis we feel the need to return for safety to some part of our past. Many Catholics today are frightened and ill at ease with the journey that has taken us so far so fast since the Second Vatican Council, and feel a need to return to something of the pre-Vatican II past. If, like Jacob, they stay close to the living God throughout the excursion, they will return enriched to the main road of the journey, as Jacob did.

Back in the Promised Land, Jacob is reconciled with his brother Esau, and takes up again the nomadic life of Abraham and Isaac, wandering from one place to another within the Promised Land.

Mary's extraordinary journey

Mary's faith journey began in a simple home in Nazareth, where the rich Jewish faith tradition was handed on to her. She learned the sacred history and hopes of her people, observed the holy leisure of the Sabbath each week and the religious feasts each year. She was shaped by the piety of a people whose only boast was their God, and whose daily life was shaped by God's law.

The angel Gabriel's message jolted Mary beyond this traditional piety with a request for something never dreamed of among her people, a virgin motherhood. To accept the call was to sacrifice her reputation and risk her marriage and her entire future. Like Abraham, she made the leap of faith into the unknown.

After the child was born she journeyed to Egypt, a pagan land where everything was alien to her. The young Jewish girl must have been shocked and broadened by her new surroundings. No doubt she was relieved when the journey brought her back to her own town, and to the ordinary tasks and joys of a wife and mother. For many years her journeys were the normal ones of a devout Jewish woman: back and forth to the well for water for her family, back and forth to the temple to celebrate the feasts.

When her grown son returned to Nazareth and preached in his own synagogue, a new stage of the journey began, one leading to Calvary. She saw her neighbors reject her son and try to kill him. She watched that hatred spread until it brought her to Calvary. There another stage of the journey began. An older woman now, of an age when she would like to have been a grandmother, she heard again an unexpected call. Jesus entrusted his beloved disciple to her. She was to become mother to the tiny Christian community which would gather in the upper room, which would receive the Holy Spirit, and which would bring the message of her son not only to Egypt, but to the whole world. The little Jewish girl had walked an extraordinary journey of faith.

Joseph: making the most of an unscheduled journey

Jacob has 12 sons. Conflict erupts among them, as it had between Esau and Jacob. The youngest son, Joseph, the dreamer, is loved by his father but not by his brothers. The jealous brothers sell him into slavery, and he retravels the road to Egypt taken by his great-grandfather Abraham. But he does not go by choice, bringing his flocks and family and servants. He is taken alone, as a slave. Yet God goes with him.

As we read Joseph's story in Genesis, we can see parallel realities in our lives. It can happen that the journey takes us by force where we have no desire to go. Illness, divorce, loss of a loved one are all tragedies which bring us to a new stage of life which we desire no more than Joseph desired to go to Egypt. Yet, when the trauma has been passed through, we may find, like Joseph, that the new world is one in which we can grow in unexpected ways, and serve others in ways we never dreamed. Because Joseph becomes a high government official in Egypt, he is able to save his entire family when famine again comes to Canaan. They follow him into the fertile land of the Nile.

Moses and Joshua: onward to freedom

In Egypt, the descendants of Jacob multiply. But a change in the political regime transforms them from honored guests into an oppressed minority group, reduced to slavery, spending their lives on the mighty construction projects of the Pharaoh. They seem to have lost both the freedom and the faith of their father Abraham. Later, the black slaves of America would identify with the oppressed Israelites.

But when the oppression becomes intolerable, God prepares a man, Moses, to free the people and lead them out of the great civilization which has become a prison for them. He leads them first into the Sinai desert. To travel through that area today is to gain a new appreciation of God's skill in the selection of stage setting. It is the most desolate place imaginable. There is nothing soft or green to ease the eye. Great rock formations and mountains or rock on every side create a sense of awe. God is purifying his people from the decadence of Egypt, forcing them to become strong and to learn to depend on him alone.

The Israelites wander 40 years through the desert, with no maps, no skills for desert survival, often hungry and thirsty, sometimes bitten by serpents. They are often afraid. But during those desert days they grow into a people.

When they have been sufficiently shaped by the desert, the people come to a new stage of the journey, the River Jordan, across which they must pass to enter the land promised to Abraham. Moses has completed his part of the journey. Joshua, the warrior, is the leader this new stage requires. He leads them into the land which is God's gift to them. Yet, it is a land for which, paradoxically, they have to fight for generations before they actually control it. Such conflicts and times of testing are not foreign to modern men and women. Our journey, too, takes us sometimes through periods of conflict in which God seems to have left us alone to fight our battles. These are dangerous times spiritually, because only the greatest of us are able to be faithful to God's law in the heat of constant battle.

David and Solomon: fleeting prosperity

The battles are finally won, and David leads the people into a time of peace and prosperity—the one moment when they possess a bit of the glory of this world, when they appear to have arrived. With the death of David's son, Solomon, the kingdom, established with such struggle, splits in two. Then the great powers of the Mesopotamian region conquer first the northern, then the southern kingdoms, bringing the poor defeated remnant of the people off into exile in Babylon. For many, it is the end of the journey of faith. They become assimilated among the pagans with whom they live, and forget God's call to their father Abraham. Today, too, not everyone perseveres on the journey of faith.

But for those who kept faith during dark hours, that faith deepened. Much of our Bible was written or collected during the Exile. Disaster forced believers to look back on the journey asking new questions, seeking a new depth of understanding, coming to a new and more personal relationship with God.

Purified by the Exile, a tiny band returns to their own land, no longer as the proud owners, but as vassals of one great empire after another, allowed only to worship, to study God's word, and to await the Messiah. Here the journey of the Old Testament comes to its end. Here, as Mary and Joseph travel to Bethlehem, a new phase of the journey begins.

Jesus: The journey goes on

The Gospels show Jesus on the same roads traveled by his ancestors: from Nazareth to Bethlehem in his mother's womb, from Bethlehem to Egypt to escape Herod, from Egypt back to Nazareth. Jesus grows up in the sheltered little Jewish town of Nazareth. But, like Abraham, he hears the call to leave everything familiar, and begin his journey into the unknown.

As Israel crossed over the Jordan to begin a new phase of its life, Jesus goes to the Jordan to begin his public life. After his baptism in the Jordan he is driven by the Spirit into the desert, where for 40 days he relives the spiritual experiences of his people who wandered 40 years in the desert. He recapitulates in his own experience the whole journey of the Old Testament.

He also begins the missionary journey, unknown to the patriarchs. He travels back and forth from Galilee to Judea, over routes Abraham used. But Jesus travels to bring the Good News, teaching and healing people everywhere.

After Jesus' personal journey leads him to Calvary and back to the Father, the missionary journey is continued by the Church and by each of its members. The God who called Abraham out of Haran and Jesus out of Nazareth still calls our people forward, into the unknown.

This article originally appeared as *Catholic Update* #1287 (1987), published by St. Anthony Messenger Press, Cincinnati, OH.

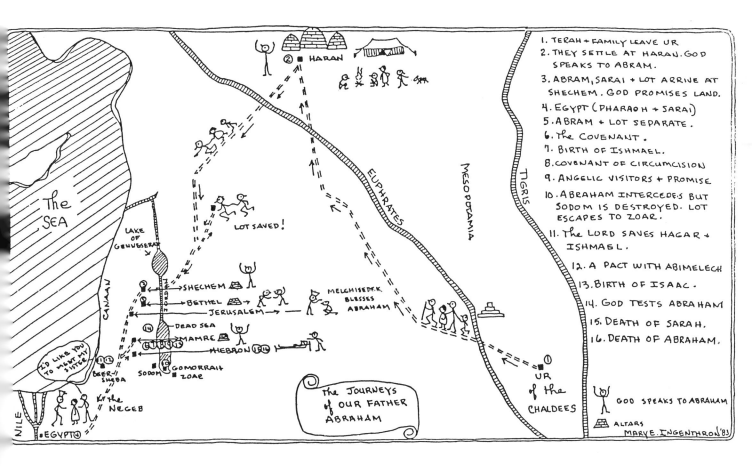

14. YAHWEH: A WARRIOR GOD?

By Dianne Bergant, C.S.A.

The questions posed by the title of this article cannot be answered easily. While the sacred Scriptures of ancient Israel frequently present Yahweh as a God of peace, there is another image that cannot be denied. Exodus 15:3 reads: "Yahweh is a warrior; Yahweh is his name." The plan to wrest the Promised Land from the people living there appears to originate with God.

> Therefore I have come down to rescue them from the hands of the Egyptians and lead them out of that land into a good and spacious land, a land flowing with milk and honey, the country of the Canaanites, Hittites, Amorites, Perizzites, Hivites and Jebusites. (Ex 3:8)

How is one to understand such a tradition, especially at a time when women and men of faith are looking to the Scriptures for inspiration and direction in their search for peace? The issue is further complicated when we admit that there are vastly different reasons for engaging in armed conflict. Wars of aggression cannot be compared with struggles for liberation and freedom. Can the biblical tradition speak to the contemporary problem of armed conflict? Is there more than one way of understanding the Bible's statements about war?

Questions

One must look to the context out of which ancient Israel speaks of Yahweh the Warrior and of the "Holy War." This context can be examined from literary, historical, and theological points of view: (1) Are the descriptions found in the text merely literary inventions intended to portray deeper religious perceptions? (2) Do they report actual events which have been embellished in transmission?

(3) Are they conditioned by ancient culture in expressing God's protection over Israel? (4) Do they perhaps contain elements of all three perspectives? We will return to these questions later.

A second set of questions must be addressed. What is one to make of this conception of Yahweh as warrior? Is it merely an unrefined image of God that Israel eventually outgrew, or was Yahweh really experienced in armed conflict? If the former is the case, does this fact undermine the revelatory value of the early traditions in the Hebrew Scriptures? If the latter is true, can war be judged unequivocally immoral? Answers to these questions do not come easily. Only by a careful examination of the tradition can one hope to throw light on the complexity of the issue.

Literary Expression

The early liturgical expressions of Israel show that the central theme of celebration was the victory of Yahweh over cosmic and/or historical enemies. Psalm 24:8 illustrates this:

> Who is this King of glory?
> The LORD, strong and mighty.
> the LORD, mighty in battle.

There are two major approaches to the interpretation of the theme of Yahweh the warrior. It is enough to say that they both deal with relationships between the literary pattern used in the narrative and the theology expressed by that pattern. The mythical pattern, very common in the ancient near eastern world, describes the primordial battle between two gods. One of the gods is the embodiment of order and the other is a comparable embodiment of chaos. Chaos is conquered and its forces are restrained, while the warrior god confirms the cosmic order that had been threatened, enters victoriously into the city, and takes up residence in the temple-palace, thereby establishing peace. In Israel's celebration, the oppressive powers of Egypt and the Canaanite city states were regarded as the concrete embodiment of cosmic chaos, and the characteristics of the valiant warrior were attributed to Israel's God. The structure and imagery of the mythical pattern shaped Israel's ritual celebration of its history. An example of this cosmic battle is found in the ancient hymn to Yahweh with Psalm 89:10-11:

> You rule over the surging of the sea;
>> you still the swelling of its waves.
> You have crushed Rahab with a mortal blow;
>> with your strong arm you have scattered
>> your enemies.

Historical Account

Besides liturgical references to a divine battle, the Hebrew Scriptures are replete with accounts of wars fought by Yahweh. One group of narratives, usually referred to as the Exodus-Conquest tradition, includes stories of both liberation from oppression and wars of aggression. In both instances Yahweh is in the forefront leading the people, and the final victory belongs to the divine warrior.

The Exodus tradition has been called the story of liberation from oppression. The earliest descriptions of Israel's valiant God refer to Yahweh as the one "who brought us out of Egypt with his strong hand and outstretched arm" (Dt 26:8). If there was violence it was in the cause of justice and only as a last resort. The victimized people cried out for release, and Yahweh intervened as warrior in order to be their Savior. The ritual reenactment of the Passover continues to be a celebration of deliverance rather than of conquest. Throughout other Israelite traditions one reads again and again of the claim that Yahweh will continually intervene in history on behalf of the

exploited (see Amos 2:6-7). Faced with the exploitation and victimization of one person or group by another, the Scriptures looked upon acts of liberation as Yahweh's intervention in history. Can such armed conflict be justified? It appears that the only way for a people to reestablish order and assure peace in such situations is to conquer chaos and restrain its forces. It is no wonder that liberation movements today turn to the Exodus tradition for inspiration and affirmation.

The Conquest narratives provide an even greater dilemma. By and large, they depict aggressive campaigns, and it is here that the image of Yahweh the Warrior and the theme of Holy War are the strongest. This is especially true in the first twelve chapters of the Book of Judges. Some recent scholarship claims that Israel's settlement in the Promised Land included more than military conquests. Slaves in revolt against petty kings, mercenary troops, oppressed serfs all joined forces with Israel. Other groups in Canaan allied themselves to Israel by treaty or were already related by ancestral ties. These disparate groups accepted the leadership of Joshua and began to worship Yahweh as supreme God and Savior. Under David and Solomon they were clearly subdivided among the traditional twelve tribes of Israel.

If this was the case, then when the ancestors of Israel threw off the domination of these overlords, their struggle for self-determination and the possession of the land wherein they were living was a struggle for liberation much as the Exodus was for those people who came out of Egypt. This interpretation sheds an entirely different light on the meaning of the Conquest. But even those holding this view admit to the reality of wars of aggression. Hence, the problem remains of Yahweh's presence and action in these wars.

Theological Interpretation

It has been said that violence is inevitable in society as we know it. Individuals and perhaps small groups may be able to transcend this inevitability, but history does not give evidence of any sovereign state being able to do so. It is difficult to imagine that Israel, among all the nations of the ancient near eastern world, was spared the horror of armed conflict. It is clear that Israel was no different from other nations in intertribal and international affairs. If there was a difference, it was in how Israel interpreted the events of history.

Three important tenets of faith are expressed in war imagery. *First,* Yahweh was the sovereign God, and so in any battle, primordial or historical, Yahweh would emerge as conqueror and would establish order and ensure peace. *Second,* Yahweh was personally present in the lives of the people as a patron God of the nation. Therefore, in times of great crisis, Yahweh was present, leading the people to victory, security, and prosperity. *Third,* other tribes or nations that threatened Israel were seen as a threat to Yahweh as well. These other people were thereby enemies of Yahweh and deserved to be punished as such. Thus, the sovereignty of Yahweh, the personal dimension of covenantal commitment, and the idea of being a special people are some of the presuppositions behind ancient Israel's theological interpretation of history.

It is pointless to pass judgment on Israel's involvement in armed conflict. Our purpose is to try to understand how Israel saw such involvement as a way to appreciate Yahweh as their Savior and king. Israel's conflicts and wars may well have resulted in theological themes and imagery that we today find offensive, but we must try to grasp what was being expressed by means of these themes and this imagery.

Conclusions

Where has this study brought us? As stated earlier, the tradition can be examined from literary, historical, and theological perspectives. It is clear that some elements of the descriptions are literary inventions intended to portray deeper religious perceptions. The mythological imagery serves as an illustration of the sovereignty of Yahweh over forces of disorder, be they cosmic, national, or societal. If the ancient near eastern world conceived of a primordial cosmic battle, then Israel would show that its God was the victor. One way of dramatizing the majesty of this victorious God was to exaggerate the details of the battle and the thoroughness of the conquest. Undoubtedly, Israel employed this manner of expression. However, this explanation does not totally discount the historicity of what is being described. Israel probably did engage in defensive conflicts of liberation as well as in offensive campaigns of aggression.

There is a thin line between actually experiencing God's help in the events of history and of later interpreting secular history theologically. Did Israel merely interpret God as warrior or was Yahweh actually experienced as warrior? This is a very difficult, if not impossible, question to answer. If, as Israel believed, Yahweh was present in every event of life, then God was also present during war, and somehow Israel had to explain this presence theologically. The significant theological issue here is God's presence, not Israel's war. Also, belief in God's protection in times of strife may be explained as God's defensive, even military action on behalf of the nation. This kind of interpretation flows from a blending of historical fact, theological perception, and literary creativity. It does not explain away the historicity, but its major focus is directed towards faith that lies behind both the literary expressions and the theological themes. To believe that Yahweh is a warrior may well have been the only way for Israel to understand and explain the provident and protective presence of God in the midst of the horror of war.

We are further confronted with the very serious question of God-language. To ask: "Is Yahweh a warrior?" is not unlike asking: "Is God a father? or a mother? Is God personal? Is God just?" These questions should be rephrased rather than answered. "What is there in the designation 'just' that is like God? What is in 'personal' that is like God? What is there about being 'mother' or 'father' that is like God? Is there anything in the idea 'warrior' that can describe God?" This article proposes an affirmative response, but only if the image of a warrior-God and the theme of Holy War be seen as theological expressions, historically bound and culturally conditioned. We are obliged to search beneath this image and this theme for the more fundamental faith of Israel.

The idea of warrior-God evokes images of superior strength and uncontested victory. It also suggests that such a God should not be challenged in the future. The patronage of a warrior-God assured victory for the people and protection amidst all forms of danger. Since God waged war only in order to restrain chaos and establish peace and order, the deity should not be seen as a warmonger but a champion of justice. War was not the major divine activity, nor was it a divine preoccupation. Good order and peace that flowed from it appear to have taken precedence.

Meaning for Today

The image of warrior-God and the theme of Holy War may have been the most apt way of understanding and explaining Yahweh's uncontested superiority, ever-present providence and protection, and identification with the cause of justice and peace at a time of great crisis in ancient Israel's history. Current biblical interpretation would suggest that we look behind the ancient theological statements for the more fundamental theology that is being expressed and that we articulate that theology through images and themes more appropriate to our times. As was pointed out earlier in this article, we must not be satisfied with simply reading the narratives on the level of the story. We must discover the meaning of the story. Neither can we merely reinterpret the war ideology in support of, or in opposition to, contemporary armed conflict. Rather, we must critique the present situation in terms of both

environmental and societal order, just and lasting peace, and the degree and quality of our acknowledgment of divine supremacy. The image of a warrior-God and the theme of Holy War are no longer apt expressions of such theology.

From: *The Bible Today,* May 1983

15. HEROIC WOMEN OF THE BIBLE

By Macrina Scott, O.S.F.

As Mary, the mother of Jesus, faced the challenges of her life, I am convinced that she drew inspiration from the heroic women of the Scriptures.

Consider Mary after the Annunciation. She found herself in a frightening predicament: pregnant before her wedding day, in a small village with a very strong sense of propriety. She might be stoned to death as an adulteress. The probability was high that her fiance would reject her, leaving her disgraced for the rest of her life. Fortunately, she did not know the even greater trials that she would face as she followed this Son to the cross.

As she looked for courage to fulfill the unheard-of role of virgin mother to which God had called her, surely she must have reflected on the Jewish women of courage who had gone before her.

Sarah

In a culture that valued motherhood above any other role for a woman, Mary must have looked with special affection toward Sarah, the mother of all Jews. It was more clearly through being descended from Sarah—than from Abraham—that one belonged to the Jewish people. Let me explain. When Sarah was believed to be barren, Abraham had a son, Ishmael, by Sarah's maid Hagar. Ishmael is remembered as father of the Arab people, but he did not inherit the special blessing promised for Abraham and Sarah's descendants. Jews know they are part of the Chosen People because of their mother Sarah.

Mary, like Israelis today, passed by the tents of nomadic tribes in the Judaean desert on her way to Jerusalem. Observing the women, she could easily imagine the life of her "mother" Sarah. It was not an easy one. Each time her husband found conditions no longer to his liking—if he

didn't like where their tent was pitched, for example, or believed that God was calling him to move on—the wife was responsible for taking down the tent (which she had woven and constantly repaired) and packing it and all their belongings for the journey. In that way Sarah had left her home country around Ur, in modern Iraq, then again the area of Syria and one spot after another in the Promised Land and Egypt.

Through those strenuous years, a greater pain than homelessness overshadowed Sarah: the pain of childlessness. The pain was so great that she herself offered her maid Hagar as a kind of surrogate mother. Once Hagar had become the mother of Abraham's son, however, she became contemptuous of her mistress and clung to the child, so that Sarah's pain grew still more intense. Yet Sarah moved on from place to place with Abraham.

As Mary risked losing the security of family and native village due to her pregnancy, one can imagine her gaining courage by remembering the courage of Sarah, again and again taking down the tent and following God's call over unknown roads to new places. From Sarah, Mary could learn that God is present not only in the familiar but also in the new and unimaginable.

Women of the Exodus

Each year at Passover, Mary heard the sacred story of her people's liberation from the slavery of Egypt. She must have noticed particularly the courage of Israelite women at that time of crisis.

The midwives Shiprah and Puah. At one period when the mighty power of Pharaoh was turned against the Israelites, a helpless minority within the great nation of Egypt, only the women are said to have resisted. Pharaoh ordered the midwives to kill the baby boys at birth. At the risk of their own lives, they refused (Exodus 1:17). The mighty Pharaoh is never dignified in the Scripture by being called by name, but the midwives, Shiprah and Puah, are so recorded as models of women who risk everything to protect new life.

Jochebed, Miriam and Pharaoh's daughter. Since Pharaoh could not control the midwives, he sent soldiers to kill the baby boys. No one had courage to resist the soldiers except one mother, Jochebed, and her young daughter Miriam. Jochebed carefully hid her infant Moses in a water-proofed basket among the reeds at the edge of the Nile River. It was all she could do, but she depended on the help of two other women, her daughter Miriam and, amazingly, the daughter of Pharaoh himself.

Miriam watched as Pharaoh's daughter came as usual to bathe in the Nile. When the princess saw the beautiful infant crying, her heart was moved and she became bonded with Jochebed and Miriam in a silent conspiracy for life, resisting with them her father's decree of death. The bonding of these women, Israelite and Egyptian, proved stronger than the death-dealing power of Pharaoh.

As Mary remembered how the midwives, Jochebed, Miriam and Pharaoh's daughter risked their lives by resisting Pharaoh to protect the Hebrew infants, she gathered the courage she would need to resist Herod and to protect her Son.

Deborah

From the hills around Nazareth, Mary could see one striking mountain rising out of the plain of Esdraelon: Mount Tabor. It brought back the memory of one of the heroes of Israel's pioneer days, when they were still in the process of conquering the land from the native Canaanites.

As in the days of our Wild West, stable structures did not yet exist. There was no organized government or standing army. So, when an enemy threatened the people, God would raise up a leader to meet the emergency. These leaders were called judges, but they were military leaders as well as settlers of disputes.

To the astonishment not only of Israel but of all the nations around her, one of these charismatic leaders raised up by God was a woman: Deborah, wife of Lappidoth. She was honored as a prophetess, and Israelites came with their disputes to the place where she sat and gave judgments under a palm tree.

When Deborah, who was in touch with all that happened among her people, realized that the Canaanite general Sisera was terrorizing the Israelite farmers with his 900 iron chariots, the most sophisticated weapons existing, she sent a message to the Israelite Barak, son of Abinoam, "This is what the Lord, the God of Israel, commands. Go, march on Mount Tabor, and take with you ten thousand Naphthalites and Zebulunites. I will lead Sisera...out to you at the Wadi Kishon, together with his chariots and troops, and will deliver him into your power" (Judges 4:6-7).

So great was Deborah's reputation that Barak did not dare ignore her summons. But he had no enthusiasm for leading a hastily gathered army of Israelite farmers and fishermen with makeshift weapons against the iron chariots of Sisera. He replied to Deborah, "If you come with me I will go; if you do not come, I will not go" (Judges 4:8). Deborah went with him, giving the army courage and wise guidance till they overcame the oppressor and were again able to live in peace.

Mary must have marveled at the courage of a wife and mother who could take on a leadership role unheard-of for women. Mary could draw upon her memories of Deborah in exercising a role of leadership in the Christian community after Jesus' death.

Naomi and Ruth

As Mary gathered in the Upper Room with followers of Jesus after the Ascension, they celebrated together the Jewish feast of Pentecost. During that celebration it was customary to listen to the reading of the Book of Ruth. This was the familiar and well-loved tale of two strong, loyal women, who preserved the life of a Jewish family through a time of disaster.

Naomi, her husband and two sons had been forced by hard times to leave their home in Bethlehem. They crossed the eastern border of their country and settled in the more prosperous land of Moab, as so many cross the Rio Grande today to seek work in the United States.

Moab was a pagan land particularly despised by the Jews, so Naomi's heart probably ached when her two sons married Moabite women. But that was only the beginning of her trials as a displaced person in Moab. Her husband died. Then her sons died without having children. In a society which saw a woman's purpose in life as bearing children who would continue her husband's life into the future, Naomi was a total failure.

At this point of personal disaster, she heard that times had improved in her hometown, so she decided to return there in her misery. She suggested that her Moabite daughters-in-law go back to their mothers, who would be able to arrange marriages for them as she could not hope to do.

One daughter-in-law did return to her mother after tearful farewells to Naomi, who had won the girls' love. Her return was sensible, as Moabites were so hated by the Israelites that she could not expect to be welcomed or to find a husband in Bethlehem.

Nevertheless, the other daughter-in-law, Ruth, refused to abandon Naomi. She insisted on leaving everything that was familiar to her to travel with her mother-in-law to Bethlehem. In Bethlehem, she began to support Naomi and herself by the backbreaking work of the poor, gleaning the bits of grain missed by the harvesters. Old Testament law forbade farmers from going a second time over their harvested fields to pick up any grain that was missed or dropped. That must be left for the poor, such as Ruth and Naomi. Boaz, the owner of the field where Ruth began her gleaning, followed more than the letter of the law, however. He

ordered his workers to treat the young Moabite with courtesy and even to drop extra handfuls of grain so that she would have a good amount to bring back to Naomi.

Day after day Ruth worked in the fields of Boaz. Boaz was touched by her loyalty toward her mother-in-law, and also by her beauty.

Wise Naomi watched and encouraged developments. Finally, thanks to her cleverness and the charm of Ruth, the kind and wealthy Boaz married Ruth. With the birth of their first son, Naomi was filled with a joy that made up for all the pain.

Mary, like all Jewish women, must have loved the story of these brave, loyal women—one Jewish and the other Gentile. From them was descended David and, ultimately, Mary's own son Jesus.

Ruth and Naomi were models for a kind of strength quite different from that of Deborah the judge. It was the loving strength of women faithful to each other and to their role of continuing the life of the family despite poverty, exile and the death of their husbands and sons. Mary needed such strength as she coped with poverty, exile in Egypt, and the death of her husband and son.

The mother of the seven martyrs

When Mary stood beneath the cross, another story from her Jewish heritage must have come to her mind. The Second Book of Maccabees tells of a mother of extraordinary strength. When the pagan King Antiochus Epiphanes tried to force the Jews to violate their sacred law by eating pork, seven brothers were arrested with their mother. Starting with the eldest, each brother in turn was interrogated, tortured, and killed in the presence of the others. The mother, speaking Hebrew, which the king did not understand, encouraged her sons. "I do not know how you came into existence in my womb; it was not I who gave you the breath of life, nor was it I who set in order the elements of which each of you is composed. Therefore, since it is the Creator of the universe who shapes each one's beginning ... he in his mercy will give you back both breath and life because you now disregard yourselves for the sake of his law" (2 Maccabees 7:22, 23).

When only the youngest son was left, the tyrant made a special effort to persuade him not only by fear of torture but also by promises of wealth and high office. Antiochus asked the mother to influence the boy to save his life. Instead, she said to him in Hebrew, "Son, have pity on me, who carried you in my womb for nine months.... I beg you, child, to look at the heavens and the earth and see all that is in them; then you will know that God did not make them out of existing things.... Do not be afraid of this executioner, but be worthy of your brothers and accept death, so that in the time of mercy I may receive you again with them."

The son rejected the tyrant's offer and was killed. Last of all, the mother herself was martyred. Hers is one of the earliest witnesses we have to a clear belief in life after death. Mary needed this great woman's faith in a resurrection to come, as well as her incredible courage, as she stood at the cross.

Esther

After Pentecost, Mary and the other women of the first Christian community may well have wondered what their role would be. As they searched the Scriptures for light on that question, they must have been struck by two biblical books that showed women as saviors of Israel, but in very different ways: Esther and Judith.

A Christian woman like Joanna, wife of the steward of Herod Antipas, ruler of Galilee (Luke 8:3), was in a position to do much for the Church through her influence over her highly placed husband. She knew that most women in Jewish history had exerted power indirectly, through male members of their families. The popular story of Esther showed how important that kind of influence could be. Esther was an orphan who had been raised by her uncle Mordecai. When the Persian king became angry with his queen, Vashti, he divorced her without scruple. But then he was lonely. So he called for a national beauty contest, searching the land for the most beautiful women. The Jewess Esther was one of the winners chosen for the king's harem. Just as she had always obeyed her foster father Mordecai, she obeyed the eunuch who was in charge of the harem. He put her through a year of beauty treatments, required before a girl could be brought in to the king. Finally, she was chosen by the king from all his women to become queen.

Esther comes across as a delicate girl, submissive to the men who control her life, more inclined to faint in time of crisis than to take action. But Esther's greatness comes from her response in a moment of crisis, a response in contrast to her natural bent and usual behavior. The king has been manipulated by the wicked Haman into passing a decree that all Jews of his kingdom should be killed. Her uncle Mordecai discovers the scheme and sends a message to Esther telling her to plead with the king for her people.

The king has grown tired of Esther, however; he has not sent for her for a month. For anyone, even the queen, to come into the king's presence without an invitation was punishable by instant death. Typically, as a woman of her times, Esther never thinks to complain about the king's fickleness, and she is terrified at the idea of entering the king's presence uninvited. But her uncle commands her sternly and, under pressure from him, she does finally go in to the king. Her terror is so great, however, that the minute she enters she faints. Her "feminine" weakness serves her well; the king is moved, and is persuaded by Esther to save her people and to destroy the enemies who had plotted their destruction. Mary would have certainly admired Esther's commitment to the welfare of God's people.

Esther is like many women who willingly remain in the background, exerting great power for good through their influence on members of their family. Joanna and some other women of the early Church found themselves in situations like hers.

For Further Study

Sarah: Genesis 12, 16, 18, 20 and 21
Miriam: Exodus 2:1–10; 15:1–21; Numbers 12
Deborah: Judges 4 and 5
Naomi and Ruth: The Book of Ruth
Esther: The Book of Esther
Judith: The Book of Judith (in Catholic Bibles only)
The mother of the seven martyrs: 2 Maccabees
    (in Catholic Bibles only)
Mary: Luke 1 and 2; John 2:1–2 and 19:25–27
Mary Magdalene: Luke 8:1–3; John 20:1–18
Joanna: Luke 8:1–3 and 24:10

Judith

Perhaps other women of that first Christian community saw their role in the Church quite differently. Mary Magdalene, for instance, has traditionally been considered to have functioned in a much more independent way. She could have found justification for that style in the Book of Judith.

Judith is woman as hero (not a heroine, waiting to be saved by a gallant hero, but one who was herself a savior of her whole people). She was a widow, a circumstance that allowed some measure of independence for a woman in biblical times. It is not said that she had any children, nor is she related to any famous leader. She is a powerful woman in her own right. When the men of her native town are ready to despair and surrender their town to the wicked general Holofernes who is besieging them, Judith protests their cowardice in strong terms. They are embarrassed by her, but helpless. Their proposal is that she should pray that God will send rain to relieve their thirst, since the besieging army has cut off their water supply.

That was their idea of a woman's role, but Judith had a different idea. In a world which saw women as perpetual minors, dependent in every way on men, taking no part in public affairs, she conceived a brilliant plan for the deliverance of the city. Then she executed it with the help of only one servant woman, and personally killed the general Holofernes, throwing his army into such consternation that they were easily routed by the Jews. She is the woman who does not work through men, but takes mighty affairs into her own capable hands. Jesus' mother, along with Mary Magdalene and other self-reliant women of the early Church, must have been impressed with her story.

Today

The women of the Bible have not lost their relevance. As women and men in the Church today hear the call to new roles, they need courage as Mary did. Like her, they can find it by looking back to the mothers of our faith found in the pages of Scripture. Catholics are moving out of old paths into new ones, as Sarah moved on till old age. Some are struggling and risking to protect new life: that of the unborn and of children in need. They can find models among the women of the Exodus.

Some women are called to roles of public leadership never before filled by women, as Deborah was. Many give their lives to sustaining loving family relationships through difficult times, like Naomi and Ruth. There are still mothers who stand by courageously as their sons or daughters are tortured and killed by unjust political regimes. There are women of great commitment who exert influence through their husbands, and women who work alone.

As women and men face the new challenges and opportunities of today, all can gain strength by remembering that we come of a line of strong women.

This article originally appeared as *Catholic Update* #1288 (1988), published by St. Anthony Messenger Press, Cincinnati, OH.

16. SELF-QUIZ: THE DEUTERONOMIC HISTORY

_____ 1. Abiathar

_____ 2. Abner

_____ 3. Absalom

_____ 4. Adonijah

_____ 5. David

_____ 6. Deborah

_____ 7. Deuteronomic Historian

_____ 8. Eli

_____ 9. Gideon

_____ 10. Hannah

_____ 11. Ishbaal

_____ 12. Jesse

_____ 13. Joab

_____ 14. Jonathan

_____ 15. Joshua

_____ 16. Michal

_____ 17. Nathan

_____ 18. Rahab

_____ 19. Samson

_____ 20. Samuel

_____ 21. Saul

_____ 22. Sisera

_____ 23. Uriah

a. Only surviving priest of Nob

b. Used ancient oral tales and written sources and composed them into great historical work

c. Canaanite leader, defeated by Deborah and Barak, slain by Jael

d. Son of Saul, friend of David

e. Daughter of Saul

f. Father of David

g. Judge who inspired Barak to battle against Sisera

h. A Nazirite whose birth was promised to his mother, the wife of Manoah

i. Leader in the conquest of promised land

j. Harlot of Jericho

k. Judge who destroyed his father's altar to Baal and led Israel against the Midianites

l. Husband of Michal, Abigail, Bathsheba, Haggith, etc.

m. Murdered his brother, Amnon

n. Tried to seize the kingdom from David after the death of Absalom

o. Anointed by Samuel, but lost his favor

p. Judge, priest and prophet

q. Was murdered on David's order

r. Mother of Samuel

s. Saul's son and successor after Saul's death

t. Saul's general, made Ishbaal king

u. David's general, murderer of Abner

v. Priest at Shiloh, teacher of Samuel

w. Prophet who delivered a reprimand and a promise of blessing to David

[Answers to this quiz may be found above on p. 82.]

17. ELIJAH: ZEALOUS FOR THE LORD

By Marilyn Norquist

Your first aim in reading about Elijah is to enjoy him. Relish the drama of the man. Don't ask questions about how the incidents really happened—we have only the stories as given and can no longer reach much behind them. But they are wonderful stories. Why not read them right now? You'll find them in 1 Kings 17–19,21, and 2 Kings 1–2.

Elijah must have inspired amazement and awe in all who saw him. Those who believed in Yahweh were thrilled with him. Those who did not found him a terrifying enemy. And no wonder! He had a habit of appearing and disappearing without warning. Miraculous events seemed to follow him around. He did everything in a big way. Even today many consider him the greatest of all the prophets.

Background to Elijah the Man

We don't know about Elijah's background or his call to be a prophet of Yahweh. We have only shreds of his preaching. But what we do know about him and his message offers its own power to us.

Elijah lived in northern Palestine, in Israel, about 850 years before Jesus. It was hardly a peaceful time. To understand the main thrust of Elijah's vehement work, we must look further back into Israelite history. When the Israelites entered Palestine after their years of desert wanderings, they were pledged to worship Yahweh only. That was the covenant made at the holy mountain. But worshiping Yahweh alone caused questions when they entered Palestine. They did not yet understand that Yahweh was the *only* God. They viewed Yahweh as one among many, and though they were committed to him, they had definite ideas about his limitations. They had experienced him as a nomadic god, who traveled around with them in the desert, directing them to food and water. But

in Palestine they became an agricultural people. They needed a god who controlled the fertility of land and animals, who sent rain and sunshine in proper distribution.

Palestine already had such gods. So the conflict was on. It raged for centuries. As early as 850, Elijah states the issue with characteristic bluntness (1 Kings 18:21). Who has power over the forces of the earth like rain and fire? Who can keep us alive in an agricultural world?

Elijah's First Mission

In Elijah's time this conflict was aggravated by two circumstances. One was King Ahab, or rather more exactly his Queen Jezebel. She had been a princess in Sidon where Yahweh was nothing; and one of the agricultural gods was the object of devotion. She brought her cult with her, converted King Ahab, and imported hundreds of her priests. Our historian makes his estimate of Ahab's character in 1 Kings 16:30-33. Doubtless Elijah agreed with him!

The second circumstance that intensified the religious crisis was drought. People were starving. Who caused it? Yahweh flings his Word through Elijah like a battle cry (1 Kings 17:1). From then on, Elijah is out to prove that power for fertility is Yahweh's alone.

Our writer sets up his scenario skillfully. He illustrates how intimate Elijah and Yahweh were (1 Kings 17:2–9). He shows both the severity of the famine and Elijah's power under Yahweh (1 Kings 17:24). Now we are readied for the drama.

Does Elijah prove his point by theological argument? No. He proposes a contest—and a big one. It will cost his life if he loses. It involves hundreds of opponents. But with Elijah stands Yahweh. For the prophet, that is enough. The story is told in 1 Kings 18. As you read, take note of the revealing details. And look for the human side of things. You may find Obadiah a humorous man who talks too much. (Yes, it's really OK to laugh with Scripture when it's funny!) Notice in 18:17 the implacable opposition between Ahab and Elijah—Ahab believes, of course, that Elijah caused the drought. That's quite an attribution of power, isn't it? Elijah gives his enemies equal opportunity. Or is it that he wants their defeat to be the more obvious? Anyway, he doesn't leave them alone. He goads (18:27). Nothing goody-goody about this prophet!

After the all-day commotion of the prophets who represented their god, Baal, our writer's final comment is simple and quiet (last half of 18:29).

Then Elijah, with consummate reverence and an unmatchable sense of the dramatic, prepares his half of the contest (18:30-35). Not enough to put out the sacrifice, though—he has to drench everything to make it as hard as possible to win! No dancing around for Elijah, either. We see him standing quietly, in dignity offering his prayer to Yahweh (18:36–37). The answer comes directly, plainly (18:38). The people see and know (18:39). Then followed the severe aftermath (18:40), which a present-day reverence for life finds repugnant.

But the central issue continues. Now it is time, and Elijah knows what the Lord will do next (18:41). He directs Ahab to enjoy his picnic, because the drought is almost over. So the rain comes—but only in accord with the word of Yahweh (17:1). Now the truth is clear: Yahweh alone controls nature.

A further note: Whatever Elijah's age, he must have been a vigorous man. Consider his big day: He went to Ahab; spent all day with the Baal priests; concluded the contest; had 450 men executed; and then when the storm threatened, ran before a horse-drawn chariot from Mt. Carmel to Jezreel (check that distance in an atlas; it may surprise you).

So the first mission of the prophet Elijah is to declare unmistakably that Yahweh is God of nature.

Note that Yahweh doesn't insist on total reform. Nor does he expect from people of that time and place a twentieth century Christian respect for life. He simply makes one point: Yahweh-God controls the rain. Yahweh always comes to his people at the point of their most immediate need for understanding. He meets us where we are.

Elijah's Second Mission

The second mission of Elijah is told in 1 Kings 21. Again, note the skill of the writer. Ahab's character is exposed (21:4). How would you describe it? The queen has even fewer scruples than Ahab, and she connives to get the vineyard for him. When the king goes down to claim it, he is met by the last man in the world he wants to see (21:20). Elijah, mincing no words, confronts Ahab: He is so straightforward, this prophet!

The second mission Elijah shares with other prophets: No matter who his hearer may be, king or slave, the prophet speaks truth. *No one* can violate the righteousness of Yahweh without consequences. This is a genius of Israelite prophecy. Other nations had "prophets" too, but they were always subject to their kings. The word of Yahweh freed the Israelite prophet to speak truth even to the king.

Praying with Elijah

Elijah's life graphically illustrates a powerful kind of prayer: the prayer of relinquishment.

After Elijah had completed his mighty day's work, one might think he would receive a reward. But no. The response to his Yahwistic proclamation terrifies him (19:2). Elijah flees. Then he prays that most potent of prayers (19:4): "I have had it! I don't want any more! You take it!" Elijah has hit bottom. From that most painful position, he gives up all his works, even his life to Yahweh. Then, Yahweh begins to care for Elijah (19:5-8). Yahweh has a word for him (19:9). Elijah's answer is true but hopeless, and he discounts others who worship Yahweh.

This great prophet is human after all! So now, after giving it all up, Elijah has his deepest experience of God (19:11-13). What tremendous lifting would be ours if we could learn from Elijah to pray before giving up—before desperation sets in.

Reflect for a moment. What is your main difficulty, your hardest perplexity? Read this passage again. In your imagination stand beside Elijah in the cave. Are you looking for God in a dramatic storm that changes your circumstances? Or in large events that seem to rock your foundations? Do you expect him to purify you and everyone else with strong flame? Elijah heard God in a tiny breath of sound. He must have been totally attentive to perceive that small whisper. Perhaps that is how God will come to you. Listen! Then give your perplexity to him.

Once again the question, "What are you doing *here*?" And Yahweh's answer to Elijah's pain is, "Go on back. You are not the only one (19:18). I still need you." Elijah goes. Now he speaks with increased power. And the price on his head? It isn't even mentioned again.

Experience of God is always prayer. This kind of prayer is gift, usually coming when we have surrendered. In giving up to God, we always find him. Or rather, he finds us and we know it.

Pray with this story about Elijah until you sense its meaning for your own life. Repeat it as often as you like. Savor Elijah's experience. Then perhaps, in some secret way especially fitted to you, you will receive a portion of his spirit (2 Kings 2:9–12).

Questions to Answer

As you read about Elijah, think about these questions:

1. His whole life was spent convincing people of certain truths about God. Was it worth it? Would it be worth *your* whole life?

2. List the references which show Elijah's obedience to Yahweh's Word. Do we obey? Does disobedience prevent our recognizing God's guidance?

3. What is Elijah's status in God's eyes? (Careful with this!)

Family Suggestions

When the family gathers, first read aloud the stories about Elijah just for enjoyment. Note any questions, but research them later. At the end of each story, you will want to share reactions. Did you like the story? Do you like Elijah? How about the other characters?

Now check maps for an idea of the places, distances, and terrain Elijah knew. In your Bible dictionary and atlas, you may find pictures, too.

Read this chapter with the Elijah stories using the references and explanations. Pay attention to the details—every one of them is important. Be sure you *all* understand the two main themes of Elijah's work. You may want to put them in your own words.

If your children enjoy dramatics, the contest on Mt. Carmel makes a wonderful playlet. You may do it several times so each child gets a chance to play Elijah. Do it with verve and abandon. Revel in it! (Perhaps your fastest-talking child should play Obadiah!) Before the playlet, discuss whether you want to act out the slaughter of the 450 prophets. Think of similar examples of killing around the world today (there are several), and discuss how far our own culture has developed a really Jesus-inspired reverence for life.

Pray together, following this chapter's suggestions. Discuss what it means to give up. How is it done? Use sports analogies, if you like, or other situations in which the children have experienced surrendering. Can you do that with God? Then find together your toughest problem in family life. Be honest. Perhaps you will want to give it up to God as a family. When you pray together then, put it in his lap and leave it there. Then you may thank him for what he is doing with it. Watch for the answer— it may come even sooner than you expect!

From: *How to Read and Pray the Prophets*, by Marilyn Norquist, Handbook of the Bible Series—Liguori Publications

FOUR YEAR PLAN OF STUDY IN THE CATHOLIC BIBLICAL SCHOOL

BIBLICAL BOOKS	GENERAL ISSUES	THEOLOGICAL THEMES

FIRST YEAR: OLD TESTAMENT FOUNDATIONS – GENESIS THROUGH KINGS

	BIBLICAL BOOKS	GENERAL ISSUES	THEOLOGICAL THEMES
UNIT 1	Exodus Leviticus Numbers	Sources of the Pentateuch	People of God Covenant/Law Desert
UNIT 2	Deuteronomy Genesis	Form Criticism Fertile Crescent	Creation/Sin Promise/The Land
UNIT 3	Joshua Judges 1 and 2 Samuel 1 and 2 Kings	Geography of Palestine Canaanite Religion Biblical Chronology Biblical Archeology	Charismatic Leadership Kingship Prophecy

SECOND YEAR: NEW TESTAMENT FOUNDATIONS – JESUS AND DISCIPLESHIP

	BIBLICAL BOOKS	GENERAL ISSUES	THEOLOGICAL THEMES
UNIT 1	Mark Luke Infancy narratives	Synoptic Question Form Criticism Redaction Criticism	Discipleship Holy Spirit
UNIT 2	Acts Pauline Letters	New Testament Geography Letter as a Literary Form	Church Gifts of the Spirit
UNIT 3	John Apocalyptic passages from the Gospels Revelation	Apocalyptic Writing	Sacraments Eschatology

THIRD YEAR: OLD TESTAMENT CONTINUED – EXILE AND RESTORATION

	BIBLICAL BOOKS	GENERAL ISSUES	THEOLOGICAL THEMES
UNIT 1	Amos Hosea I Isaiah Micah Zephaniah Nahum Jeremiah	Biblical Chronology	Prophetic Vocation Social Justice Marriage of God and Israel
UNIT 2	Lamentations Obadiah Ezekiel II Isaiah Haggai Zechariah 1–8 III Isaiah Ezra Nehemiah		Destruction of Temple Exile Renewal After the Exile Community Rebuilt Around the Word
UNIT 3	Chronicles Joel Malachi Ruth Song of Songs Psalms	History Writing in OT Hebrew Poetry Jewish Liturgy	

FOURTH YEAR: BOTH TESTAMENTS CONCLUDED – THE WORD IN THE HELLENISTIC WORLD

	BIBLICAL BOOKS	GENERAL ISSUES	THEOLOGICAL THEMES
UNIT 1	Proverbs Habakkuk Job Ecclesiastes Sirach Wisdom	Priest, Prophet, and the Wise (overview)	Creation emphasis Problem of Suffering
UNIT 2	Jonah Esther Tobit Baruch Zechariah 9–16 1 and 2 Maccabees Judith Daniel	Deuterocanonical Books Hellenism	Martyrdom Resurrection
UNIT 3	Matthew Pastoral Epistles Catholic Epistles Hebrews		Role of Peter, Apostles New Testament as Fulfillment of Old